Harlequin  *Romances*

OTHER
Harlequin Romances
by YVONNE WHITTAL

Many of these titles are available at your local bookseller
or through the Harlequin Reader Service.

For a free catalogue listing all available Harlequin Romances,
send your name and address to:

HARLEQUIN READER SERVICE,
M.P.O. Box 707, Niagara Falls, N.Y. 14302
Canadian address: Stratford, Ontario, Canada N5A 6W4

or use order coupon at back of books.

Devil's Gateway

by

YVONNE WHITTAL

Harlequin Books

TORONTO • LONDON • NEW YORK • AMSTERDAM • SYDNEY • WINNIPEG

Original hardcover edition published in 1977
by Mills & Boon Limited

ISBN 0-373-02077-5

Harlequin edition published June 1977

Printed in U.S.A.

CHAPTER ONE

Vicky Reid pushed her work aside and glanced at the telephone on her desk. If only it would ring, she thought anxiously. Conrad de Jongh's appointment with the manager of the Atlas Company had been for eight-thirty that morning and that was two hours ago, she realised as her gaze lifted to the electric clock on the wall. Surely two hours had been long enough to make the necessary arrangements?

She got tiredly to her feet and walked across to the window, her footsteps muffled by the plush carpet. She pressed her hot forehead against the cool window-pane and stared down into the street below. It was raining steadily and the water ran in little rivulets down the window, slightly distorting her view. The cars swished past on the wet tarmac, sending up a spray of water, while pedestrians either went hurriedly about their business, or huddled together under shop awnings while they waited for the buses which would take them out to their homes in the suburbs.

It was May and the winter rains had begun with a vengeance in the Cape, with the added discomfort of a strong south-easterly wind as a driving force behind it. Vicky shivered slightly and grimaced at the patches of steam left on the window by her breath.

Where had this sudden nightmare begun, she wondered distractedly, and more important, where would it end? For the whole of her twenty-six years life had been placid enough. She had an interesting job as private secretary to an architect, with a salary that allowed her to live in comfort, if not in luxury. Her evenings were spent quietly at home with an enjoyable book to read, or listening to music from the collection of records she had acquired over the years. Occasionally she went to a show or joined a few friends for dinner, and her younger brother, Michael, called on her from time to time, mostly to borrow money which he politely forgot to repay. Admittedly her life was far from exciting, yet quite happy, and Vicky had no desire to alter the rhythmic pattern of her daily routine.

The diversion from normality had begun two days ago when Hilary Jennings invited her over to have dinner with them that same evening. This in itself was quite normal, for Hilary often invited Vicky to spend a quiet evening with herself and her husband, Sam. The abnormality began at the sight of the Holden station-wagon parked outside the house, and in the presence of its owner, ensconced in an armchair in the living-room.

Hilary was her usual gay and charming self when she took Vicky through to the living-room, and Sam, too, gave her his usual welcoming smile, but it was the man who emerged from the depths of the large, heavily padded arm-chair who caught and held Vicky's attention.

She was all at once alarmingly conscious of the man's enormous height, massive shoulders tapering down to slim hips, and piercing grey eyes that pinned her to the floor and appeared to strip her of her usual spontaneity with strangers. There was a clamouring in her throat like a frightened bird fluttering in an attempt to escape at the approach of a snake.

Vaguely, Vicky was aware of Hilary making the intro-ductions. His name was Conrad de Jongh, but nothing else penetrated Vicky's numbed brain. He extended a hand, large and tanned with well-kept finger-nails, and Vicky's slim hand disappeared completely in its warm, rough clasp.

The rest of the evening was slightly unreal with a night-marish quality about it that made her uneasy, and quite often rendered her speechless. Hilary and Sam obviously

6

noticed nothing amiss, for the conversation between themselves and Conrad de Jongh flowed comfortably.

He was a friend of Sam's and they had been at school together as she and Hilary had been, Vicky understood from their conversation. He was also a farmer, she gathered, and he was spending a few days in Cape Town on business.

Seated opposite him at the dinner table, Vicky was conscious of those steel-grey eyes regarding her intently on a few occasions, and it made her feel uncomfortable and clumsy. It was only when they returned to the living-room that Vicky made use of the opportunity to take a closer look at Conrad de Jongh while Hilary poured the coffee.

He was not handsome by the usual standards, for his features were far too rugged to appeal to one in that sense. His hair was jet black with a smattering of grey at the temples, and judging hastily Vicky would say that he was nearer forty than thirty. His forehead was broad with thick, bushy eyebrows as black as his hair, and they were tapered in such a way that it appeared as though he was constantly amused by something, or someone. It was almost a shock to discover that someone with such dark hair and tanned complexion could have such light grey eyes. Added to this were his aquiline nose and square chin that jutted out stubbornly and conveyed determination and strength. His lips were perfectly chiselled with a stern look about them that gave Vicky the impression they could also be cruel. His white shirt-collar contrasted vividly with his tanned complexion, and his grey suit, although cut plainly and expertly to fit his large frame, was of expensive material. His shoes were of genuine leather and immaculately polished, and for a farmer, Vicky thought wryly, he certainly had good taste in clothing.

He turned his head slightly and their glances clashed. His inquiring, and hers guilty, at being caught staring.

'Are you always so quiet, Miss Reid?' he asked in his

deep, gravelly voice. 'Or do you possess that excellent quality of being a good listener which few women can lay claim to?'

The question, directed so suddenly at her, caught her slightly off balance and rendered her speechless. To her mortification she blushed profusely, and it was only Hilary's quick intervention that gave her the opportunity to regain her composure.

'Vicky is quiet only until you get to know her,' Hilary remarked in Vicky's defence.

'I have yet to meet a woman who is a good listener,' Sam scoffed good-naturedly, only to receive a thump on the knee from Hilary's fist. 'What was that for?' he protested laughingly.

'For your condescending attitude towards women in general,' Hilary informed him with mock severity.

Conrad de Jongh glanced at Vicky then and smiled, relieving the tension between them instantly. 'Perhaps we have been so busy talking that we did not give Miss Reid an opportunity to speak,' he suggested, his glance flicking quickly to her hands gripped tightly in her lap. 'My apologies. You must have found the conversation indescribably boring.'

'Not at all,' Vicky contradicted hastily, that same fluttering feeling at the base of her throat. 'If I have been quiet it's merely because I've been interested, and not because I've been bored.'

Conrad de Jongh accepted this with a brief nod of his head, his eyes holding hers captive for a moment longer before he returned his attention to their hosts.

Vicky could no more explain her emotions than she could those of the porcelain cat staring down at her from the mantelshelf. There had been several men in Vicky's life over the past few years, but they had come and gone without leaving even the slightest impression on her. They had been casual friends with whom she had had something in common and their relationships had been uncomplicated and uncluttered by emotions. She was independent by nature and was in no great hurry to tie herself down to the demands of a husband and the monotony of housework. Her male companions had known this and had expected nothing more than her friendship.

What troubled Vicky most at that moment was the fact that no one had ever made such an impact on her as Conrad de Jongh had from the moment they had met. What was it about the man that set her nerves jangling and caused that odd flutter in her chest and throat? Why was she suddenly emotionally alert and frightened out of her wits by something she could not even lay her finger on?

As the evening wore on Vicky began to relax a little despite these puzzling thoughts. With a supreme effort she managed to take part in the conversation and thereby gained a semblance of normality. Hilary was not fooled, though, for her questioning glance was turned several times in Vicky's direction. When Vicky finally announced that it was time she went home, Hilary looked as though she was about to protest and then changed her mind.

'If Conrad will excuse me for a few minutes I'll run you home quickly,' Sam offered, hunting for his keys.

'If Miss Reid does not object, I could give her a lift home,' Conrad de Jongh said suddenly, and Vicky, arrested in the act of putting on her wrap, could only stare as she became taut with nerves.

'May I?' he asked, taking the wrap from her passive fingers and placing it about her shoulders. 'It's time I left as well.'

In a wild rush of panic Vicky was about to refuse his offer when she noticed a glint of mockery in his eyes. It was uncanny, but she was almost certain that he had been able

9

to read her thoughts at that moment and he was challenging her to deny it.

Vicky lifted her chin and had to arch her neck considerably to meet his glance. 'It's kind of you to offer me a lift, Mr de Jongh. Thank you very much.'

Conrad de Jongh for some reason seemed to be amused. Her panic turned to anger. Let him be amused! she thought. He was nothing but a big ape, and if he thought that his size would intimidate her, then he could think again.

With these defiant thoughts she said goodnight to Sam and Hilary and allowed Conrad de Jongh to help her into the Holden. Two blocks away her defiance and courage deserted her and she was left a shivering bundle of nerves on the front seat beside his broad, imposing frame. This was ridiculous, she admonished herself quietly. So what if he was big and broad-shouldered, with hands that looked as though he could crush any living thing to a pulp without the slightest effort? Apart from his size he was no different from any of the other men she had known. Was he? This tantalising thought raced through her mind and increased her pulse rate.

He did not attempt making conversations and apart from her giving him the occasional directions to her flat, nothing was spoken between them until he parked the Holden at the entrance.

'I'll come up with you,' he said before she could wish him goodnight, and despite her protests he walked up the two flights of steps with her, his hand warm and firm beneath her elbow. His touch sent urgent and unintelligible messages to her brain which she refused to analyse and she was thankful when he removed his hand at the entrance to her flat to take the key from her. If he had noticed her slight hesitation in handing it over, he gave no indication, and she wondered frantically whether he expected her to invite him in for something to drink.

He allayed these fears of hers instantly by remarking, 'I shan't keep you. It's late and I must get back to my hotel.'

He had entered the flat with her and they now stood facing each other in the short passage that led to the lounge, and Vicky could not help noticing that he completely dwarfed the normally wide entrance. She pressed her back against the wall to avoid standing too close to him and thanked him primly for the lift. Once again it appeared as though something amused him, for she could detect that odd glint in his eyes.

'Will you have dinner with me tomorrow evening?'

The invitation was so sudden that for a moment Vicky could not reply. 'I—I don't know,' she stammered, helplessly confused by his nearness and the disconcerting look in his eyes.

'Why are you afraid of me?' he asked, and his voice was like the distant roll of thunder.

'I'm not afraid of you,' she denied, trembling inwardly.

'Then prove it by having dinner with me.'

It was a challenge Vicky could not ignore, while he was standing there obviously aware of her confusion and finding it a huge joke.

'I accept your invitation,' she said firmly, lifting her chin proudly and defiantly.

Conrad de Jongh extended his hand towards her and as her own disappeared within it he smiled, his teeth flashing white against his tanned skin. 'I shall call for you at six-thirty,' he said. 'Goodnight, Vicky.'

She placed her hand against the quivering pulse in her throat as his footsteps disappeared down the stairs. Vicky! After addressing her so formally all evening he had suddenly called her Vicky! The sound of her name on his lips had startled her, and left her strangely vulnerable.

The following morning Vicky found herself looking forward to her evening out with Conrad de Jongh with a mix-

11

ture of delight and fear, but during the course of the morning she received a telephone call that wiped all thoughts of him from her mind. The call was from Michael, and he was obviously nervous and upset.

'Vicky, can you come down to the main police station?'

Vicky was instantly alert, her hand gripping the receiver as if for support. 'Are you hurt? Has there been an accident?'

There was a moment of silence, and then Michael's voice said tremulously: 'There hasn't been an accident, Vicky. I've been arrested.'

There was a shocked silence as Vicky gathered her scattered wits about her. This must be some sort of sick joke Michael was playing, she decided, but the next instant another voice came over the line and she knew that her nightmare had become reality.

'Miss Reid, this is Detective-Inspector Johnson speaking. Your brother was arrested for fraud yesterday morning but can be released on five hundred Rand bail, providing he remains in the city until further notice.'

'Oh, no!' she moaned, subsiding into her chair to remove her weight off her trembling legs.

'I'm sorry, Miss Reid, this must be a shock to you.' The Inspector's voice sounded apologetic.

'Yes—yes, it is.'

'Do you have the means with which to bail him out?'

Vicky's thoughts flew to her meagre savings and she knew that this latest escapade of Michael's would all but diminish them to a few miserable Rand not worth mentioning.

'I—I can manage it,' she stammered, 'but I shall have to call on the bank first, and that may take time.'

'We're in no hurry, Miss Reid,' the Inspector assured her. 'We will release your brother as soon as the formalities are completed.'

Vicky arrived at the police station just before midday,

and fifteen minutes later Michael, frightened and unsure of himself, left with her. Detective-Inspector Johnson had been pleasant enough under the circumstances, but Michael's crime was of such a nature that it did not warrant light-hearted conversation. The Inspector had quite calmly stressed the fact that Michael should make himself available whenever he was called upon, and although he spoke quietly there was an underlying urgency in his voice.

'What are you going to do now?' Vicky asked as they stood together on the pavement, her glance going swiftly over Michael's crumpled suit and unshaven chin. He looked so pathetic that her tender heart softened instantly. 'Let's go to your flat so that we can talk in private,' she suggested gently.

'I don't live at the same place any more,' Michael told her dully. 'I was kicked out three months ago because I couldn't pay the rent, so in the meantime I've moved in with a pal of mine.'

Vicky momentarily closed her eyes and prayed silently for strength. 'In that case I suggest we collect your things so that you can move in with me,' she said determinedly, giving him a glance that clearly conveyed the fact that she would not be dissuaded.

It did not take much time to collect Michael's few belongings and before long they were at Vicky's flat. She made them something to eat, but neither of them was very hungry and the food remained almost untouched.

Vicky glanced at her wrist watch. It was one-thirty. 'I'm going to be late for work,' she remarked grimly, 'but first we have to talk.'

They sat facing each other in the lounge while Michael almost chain-smoked. Vicky studied him intently for a moment. He was only twenty, fair and boyish. Their parents had spoiled him, and after their deaths she had continued to do so, always giving in to his whims without the slightest rebuke. It had been a mistake, she realised. Michael had needed a firm hand right from the beginning, then he would not have landed himself in the mess he was in at that moment.

'How much?' she asked, holding her breath.

Michael could not meet her eyes. 'Five thousand Rand over a period of months.'

The room tilted and readjusted itself as Vicky clung to her chair. 'Why, Michael? Why did you do it?'

Michael lit another cigarette, his bloodshot eyes downcast. The nasty experience of being arrested was beginning to tell on him, and he had obviously been crying at some time and had rubbed the tears away with his hands, for there were dirty smudges across his cheeks.

'I've been gambling quite a lot during the past year,' he began, a slight tremor in his voice.

'But why gamble for such high stakes, in fact why gamble at all?'

Michael shifted about uncomfortably in his chair, and puffed angrily at his cigarette. 'When I first started gambling I was lucky and won quite a lot. Then I started losing, and each time I went back in the hope that I would make up what I'd lost the previous time. My salary was no longer covering my gambling expenses, so ...'

'So you stole the money,' Vicky filled in for him mercilessly.

Michael flinched at her words. 'I didn't intend stealing it, Vicky. I cooked the company's books to get the money, hoping that I would be able to replace the amount eventually, but the company took on a new accountant and he insisted on going through the books with a fine tooth comb, so to speak, and quite naturally he found out.'

'Why didn't you come to me for help?'

'I've borrowed from you so often in the past,' Michael remarked, stubbing out his cigarette and lighting another.

'If I'd asked you for this amount you would have become suspicious.'

Vicky groaned softly. 'If only you'd told me, Michael! I would have tried to get hold of the money in some way.'

There was silence in the room except for the ticking of the clock as they sat facing each other helplessly.

'What am I going to do, Vicky?'

Vicky sighed heavily, lifting her hands in despair. 'Do you think they might withdraw the case against you if you repay the money?'

'They might,' Michael replied with a shrug, 'but I wouldn't put too much faith in that if I were you. The boss can be pretty sticky at times and it won't be easy to convince him, or the authorities, that I didn't intend to steal the money, but merely to borrow it.'

'I must get back to work. Have a bath and a shave and get some rest,' she told him as she prepared to leave. 'And don't worry, I'll think of something.'

Her own words echoed hollowly through her mind for the rest of the afternoon. What was there that she could do to help him? Nothing! Where would she get five thousand Rand from in the first place, and what guarantee had she that the manager of the Atlas Comany would then withdraw the case against Michael? On several occasions during the afternoon her hand had reached for the telephone to contact Sam Jennings. He was so sensible and always gave such sound advice. Surely he could help her? Overcome with shame, she eventually abandoned the idea and plodded relentlessly through the rest of the afternoon until it was time to go home.

Michael looked at her expectantly as she entered the flat, but her expression was so bleak that he realised instantly that she had been unable to think of a solution. Dressed in denims and a faded sweater, he looked decidedly better after his rest. His chin was clean-shaven, but his expression remained haggard.

Vicky took in his appearance and her tender heart softened towards him. She placed her arms about him as she had done so many times in the past, and hugged him close to her.

'Don't worry, Michael, we'll think of something yet,' she told him gently, kissing his lean cheek affectionately.

It was then that she remembered her dinner date with Conrad de Jongh, and a feeling close to despondency took possession of her. She would have to cancel it, she thought, but she had no idea where he was staying. Michael noticed her troubled frown and when he inquired as to the cause of it, she told him of her predicament.

'Don't cancel your appointment on my behalf, Vicky,' Michael insisted. 'I'll be quite comfortable here in your flat. I'll make myself something to eat and go to bed. I'm tired and confused, and so are you. Perhaps we'll be able to think of something tomorrow,' he ended hopefully.

Vicky hesitated a moment, in a quandary as to what she should do. If she backed out now Conrad would think, as he had done the previous evening, that she was afraid of him; but if she went she would not be able to relax and enjoy herself while her thoughts were occupied with Michael.

Quite by chance the thought came to her that Conrad de Jongh, being a stranger, might be easier to approach for help than someone who was close to her. If she told him everything, taking the responsibility upon herself to repay him, he might just consider lending her the money with which she could approach the Atlas Company in the hope of quashing the case against her brother. The more she thought about it, the more excited she became.

She bathed and dressed with care after making this decision. It would not be easy to talk to Conrad de Jongh, but it would at least be a relief to speak to someone who was not directly involved. If he would not lend her the five thousand Rand, he might at least have some ideas to put forward.

Vicky chose a cream silk outfit for the evening. The neckline was daringly low, yet not outrageous. The soft folds of the material clung gently to her shapely figure and made her look even more slender than she was, while the full-length skirt added a few inches to her height.

She was not beautiful if one was interested in classic beauty. Her eyes were too big and set wide apart, her nose too short and tilted slightly at the end, and her mouth was too wide. However, if one took a closer look one would see the corn-coloured hair combed back severely and fastened at the nape of her neck while small tendrils persisted in escaping, to curl softly about her face. There was also the candid honesty in the golden-brown eyes, the perfectly modelled cheekbones and the small but firm chin. It was her mouth, however, that was her greatest asset. Although too wide, there was a sensuous curl to her lower lip that quite often displayed her vulnerability when she was hurt, but the overall impression was that of hidden passion.

Sam Jennings had once jokingly remarked that Vicky in love would be a revelation. It would be an overpowering, all-embracing emotion that would rip down the barriers she had placed about her heart like a tidal wave, and she would be borne on the crest of it throughout her life. For Vicky, once she had given her heart into one man's keeping, would show her love with her mind and body to that man only. She would love but once, and never again if her love were to be rejected.

Conrad de Jongh was as good as his word. At six-thirty sharp he rang the front-door bell. Vicky introduced him to her brother and he acknowledged the introduction with a brief nod before escorting her down to the Holden and whisking her off to the restaurant.

Vicky was nervous and depressed, and the intimate lighting in the restaurant only served to make her more aware of the fact that she would be alone in Conrad de Jongh's company for the rest of the evening. She was absolutely petrified when she thought of how she had planned to ask him for help. Now that she was sitting opposite him in this expensive restaurant with the narrow width of the table between them, her courage deserted her and left her limp at the thought of her audacity.

Conrad ordered a bottle of wine while they waited for their meal to be served and while the waiter poured the bright red liquid into delicately stemmed glasses, Vicky stared down at the glittering silverware on the snow-white damask tablecloth as though the answer to her problem lay somewhere among these expensive items.

'Your wine,' Conrad's deep voice interrupted her thoughts. Their fingers touched lightly, electrifying her nervous system. Her hand trembled slightly, spilling a drop of liquid on the tablecloth. 'Careful,' Conrad laughed teasingly. 'You haven't even tasted your drink yet. What will you be like after the second one, I wonder?'

Their eyes met across the flame of the candle and an involuntary smile plucked at her mouth and danced in her eyes. Her tenseness evaporated momentarily as she withstood his glance.

'Are you having qualms about inviting me out to dinner this evening?'

'I have no qualms, I assure you,' he stated calmly. 'If, during the course of the evening, I am forced to carry you out of here, I shan't mind at all.' His eyes glittered strangely. 'It isn't often that I have the opportunity of holding a beautiful woman in my arms, even if she happens to be in an inebriated state.'

18

Vicky sobered instantly, a pulse throbbing wildly at the base of her throat. His large hand captured hers where it lay on the table, and the warm pressure of his fingers filled her with panic.

'Did you find that rather a crude remark?' he asked, not showing any sign of regret.

Vicky shook her head, conscious only of the touch of his hand and the rapid increase in her pulse rate.

'When you've lived on a farm for as long as I have,' he observed, a glint of humour in his eyes, 'with only the labourers to talk to and the neighbours who occasionally come over for a drink and a chat, you're apt to forget how to behave in the company of a lady.'

'Please!' Vicky burst out suddenly. 'Please don't apologise.' But she was aware that he did not sound at all apologetic and felt alarmed at her own response to the thought of being held in his arms.

He smiled slowly, released her hand and lifted his glass. 'Shall we drink a toast, then? To a very charming and forgiving lady.'

Their eyes met over the rim of their glasses as they sipped the smooth liquid and, even when they had replaced their glasses on the table, Vicky could not tear her eyes away from his. There was something in his expression that both frightened and tantalised her; it filled her with an unknown excitement and a certain amount of awe.

Conrad leaned forward suddenly as though he wanted to say something, but they were interrupted by the waiter serving their dinner. The moment was gone and Vicky knew that for ever afterwards she would be left wondering what he had been going to say.

He refilled their glasses with wine and attacked his steak in silence. Vicky, too, said little throughout the meal, though she stole several surreptitious glances in his direction. He was once again immaculately dressed in a dark evening suit,

19

snow-white shirt and black bow-tie. His crisp black hair was combed back from his forehead and and he seemed to have a distinguished look she had not noticed before.

'You have been very quiet,' he remarked later as they waited for their coffee to be served. 'Is there something troubling you?'

'This is my chance,' she thought quickly, yet something held her back. Would he understand? she wondered frantically. Was he the right person to approach for help?

'Nothing is troubling me,' she lied eventually, losing her nerve and hating herself for it.

The waiter brought their coffee and Vicky poured. Her hand trembled visibly as she handed him his cup and Conrad raised a questioning eyebrow.

'You're a bad liar,' he said suddenly. 'Whatever it is that's making you tremble like that, you'd better get it off your chest. Tell me about it and perhaps I could help in some way.'

One glance in his direction made her realise that it would be useless denying his allegation. She took a sip of coffee to steady herself and then haltingly told him of Michael's predicament, omitting nothing.

For a long time after she had finished, Conrad remained silent, staring frowningly at the table while Vicky nervously played with the silver teaspoon in her saucer. All around them there was the hum of muted voices and the occasional laughter, but Vicky sat numbed in her chair, conscious only of Conrad de Jongh's brooding silence.

'I presume you would like to do something about it?' he asked eventually. 'Possibly try and get them to withdraw the case?'

Vicky nodded speechlessly.

'Do you have five thousand Rand with which to do your bargaining?'

'No. I wondered . . .' Vicky scraped the remnants of her courage together and met his glance fearlessly. 'Conrad, could you perhaps lend me five thousand Rand? I would, of course, take it upon myself to repay you. With interest, naturally,' she added breathlessly. Her words had come out in a rush and now that she had asked the dreaded question, she felt physically and mentally exhausted.

His steel-grey eyes narrowed to slits. It was impossible to know what the man was thinking as he sat forward in his chair and leaned his elbows on the table. He took his time before replying and the tension increased with every passing second.

'I'll lend you the money,' he said, but there was something in his voice that made her realise instantly that it was not going to be as easy as she had thought. 'I'll lend you the money,' he repeated ominously, 'but there are two conditions attached to it. The first one is that your brother allows himself to be placed in my custody and that he agrees to work on the farm for me to repay the loan.'

There was another tense silence during which Vicky hardly dared to breathe. 'And the other condition that you spoke of?'

Conrad's eyes glittered in the candlelight. 'You must agree to marry me.'

If several volts of electricity had shot through her body she could not have been more shocked. She opened her mouth foolishly and closed it again as his eyes pinned her helplessly to her chair.

'You can't be serious,' she croaked.

'I assure you I am,' he informed her, his lips drawn into a thin line. 'Let me put it this way. I will repay the five thousand Rand and arrange for the case against your brother to be withdrawn. He repays me by working on my farm, which will be preferable to possible hard labour in prison. At the same time I am in need of a wife. By marrying me you will also be close to your brother, which should give you some comfort.'

The pupils of Vicky's eyes were dilated as she stared at

him in horror. Married! Married to this huge man whom she had only met the previous evening? It was unthinkable! It was impossible! How could she share his home; his bed! These thoughts pounded against her temples as the cold sweat broke out on her forehead.

As if guessing her thoughts, Conrad continued: 'It will naturally not be a real marriage. Think of it as a business arrangement. Perhaps, after a year, we could discuss this matter again, and if we then feel that we could continue our marriage on a normal basis, we shall do so. If not, then I will give you an annulment and at the same time settle an amount in your name which will help you to establish yourself once more until you are able to find a suitable appointment.'

'Why should you want to marry me?' she asked, still shying away from the idea. 'I'm not even attractive.'

Conrad's glance rested on her face and then deliberately shifted lower. The blood rushed to her face and drummed in her ears.

'Let us say that you have certain attributes that appeal to me,' he replied casually, a mocking smile on his lips. 'There is one other factor I haven't mentioned. To all intents and purposes, our marriage must appear normal—even to your brother. I shall, therefore, rely upon you to indulge in a little play-acting when we find ourselves in the company of others.' He was silent for a moment, almost as though he enjoyed her embarrassment. 'It shouldn't be too difficult, should it?'

Vicky hardly knew what happened afterwards. She only knew that she had eventually agreed to marry him and that he had driven her to her flat, promising to telephone her at work the following day to tell her of the success or failure of his interview with the Atlas Company.

CHAPTER TWO

CONRAD's promised telephone call was not forthcoming as Vicky returned to her desk and endeavoured to continue with her work. What was happening at the Atlas Company that prevented him from telephoning? Another hour dragged by relentlessly and by the time the telephone eventually rang, Vicky was a bundle of nerves as she pounced on it.

'Vicky?'

'Yes.'

Conrad laughed suddenly, a deep-throated laugh that sent the blood pumping recklessly through her veins. 'Don't sound so anxious. It's all over.'

'What?' she almost shrieked. 'Did they——?'

'The manager of the Atlas Company accepted my cheque and agreed to withdraw the case against your brother,' he informed her, and she detected a note of triumph in his voice. 'The problem was persuading the authorities to do the same, but I'll spare you the details.'

A sob rose in her throat as she clung to the receiver.

'You're not crying, are you?' Conrad asked suspiciously, and then spoke more roughly. 'For goodness' sake, Vicky, it's all over. Your problems are at an end.'

'I know,' she cried unashamedly, 'and I can't thank you enough for all you've done. I'm just so happy.'

'Women!' he growled impatiently. 'I swear I shall never understand them.'

'What happens now?' Vicky asked, managing to control her tears.

'Now,' he told her, 'you go to that boss of yours and hand in your resignation. Tell him that tomorrow will be the last day you'll be working for him, that you're going to be married the day after that, and that you will be leaving Cape Town immediately after the ceremony to accompany your husband to his farm in the Karroo.'

'But I can't resign giving only a day's notice,' she protested. 'I'll lose a month's wages.'

'Will it matter?' he asked bluntly.

'My boss will never allow it,' she tried again.

'He'd better!'

Vicky capitulated when she heard the underlying threat in his muttered words. 'What happens then?' she asked timidly.

'Nothing,' he remarked casually. 'You continue with your work until five o'clock, when I shall call for you and take you home. I want to have a talk with that brother of yours to put him in the picture. Do you agree?'

'Yes.' She hesitated. 'Conrad, none of this can be very pleasant for you, and I would like you to know that I do appreciate your help.'

'Despite the conditions I mentioned?' he mocked.

Taken aback, she remained silent for a moment. 'Yes,' she admitted, surprising even herself. 'Despite everything I am still grateful for all you have done.'

A throaty chuckle came over the line and Vicky blushed furiously. 'I think you'll like Duiwelspoort,' he remarked suddenly. 'Goodbye.'

'Duiwelspoort'. Was that the name of his farm? she wondered as she replaced the receiver.

The task of handing her employer her resignation and saying that she wished to be released from her duties almost immediately was more difficult than she had anticipated. Although he agreed to release her, he spent almost ten minutes lecturing her on the pitfalls of marrying with such haste. He ended by telling her that there would always be a post for her with the company if things did not work out and she wished to return. Vicky thanked him profusely and hurried back to her own office lest he should see his usually efficient secretary succumb to womanly tears.

During the course of the afternoon, as the work diminished on her desk, the enormity of what she had done struck her like a blow between the eyes. To help Michael she was about to relinquish her freedom, her comfortable, stable life, to marry a man who was an absolute stranger to her. What had she done? What had possessed her to agree to Conrad's outrageous suggestion? Should she have sacrificed herself even for Michael's freedom? she wondered in despair, covering her face with her hands. It was too late now to retract the promise she had given. Michael was free, Conrad had seen to that, and now she had to fulfil her part of the bargain as best she could.

Conrad was leaning against the wall in the foyer, smoking a pipe, when Vicky emerged from the lift shortly after five. He pushed his pipe unceremoniously into his jacket pocket and helped her into the Holden parked outside. The odour of pipe tobacco clung to him as he slid his big frame behind the wheel, and Vicky found it strangely pleasant.

With nothing more than a cursory glance in her direction he edged the Holden into the stream of traffic and drove through the city at a leisurely pace. It was still raining steadily and drops of water glistened on his hair, she noticed during the ensuing silence. It was not until he missed the turning to her flat that Vicky spoke for the first time.

'You'll have to turn right at the next corner,' she told him calmly. 'You missed——'

'I didn't miss anything,' he interrupted, equally calm, and when she glanced at him with quick alarm he continued, 'I'm taking you to a little place I've heard of where they make an excellent cup of coffee, and where it's quiet enough to discuss a few things without being disturbed.'

'Oh.' Vicky relapsed into silence.

The low drone of the Holden's engine lulled her into a relaxed frame of mind, and she was astonished to discover that she was no longer nervous in Conrad's company. He looked, if nothing else, strong and dependable as he sat beside her, his attention directed on the road ahead. His hands resting on the wheel were strong and capable, with fine black hairs on the back. They were labourer's hands, tanned by the sun and roughened by work. He was a giant of a man, but she no longer found this alarming, only curiously comforting. The only thing that still caused her slight discomfort was the peculiar effect he had on her emotions when his grey eyes regarded her with such intensity.

What was he really like? she wondered as she glanced at him surreptitiously. She was marrying him to save her brother from a prison sentence, and this thought must be just as distasteful to him as it was to her. It would be a marriage in name only, he had said. A business arrangement. But what guarantee had she that he would honour the agreement between them? By the set of his jaw and the firm line of his lips she was sure that he could be quite ruthless if the need arose.

Vicky shivered slightly at the trend of her thoughts, and tried instead to visualise his farm and what her new home would look like.

Conrad turned off the main road on to a secondary road and before long he parked at the entrance to a windmill-shaped coffee bar. Neither of them spoke a word until they were seated at a corner table and Conrad had ordered their coffee.

'Did you hand in your resignation?' he asked without preamble.

Vicky lowered her glance. 'Yes, I did.'

'Good.'

26

Conrad said nothing more until their coffee arrived and they were once more left alone.

'The two people who are going to be the most difficult to convince that our marriage is genuine,' he continued, 'will be Sam and Hilary.'

Vicky nodded, her throat tightening. 'What are we going to do?'

A flicker of a smile crossed his face. 'We shall just have to appear very affectionate in their company, and we'd better plan now what we're going to tell others so that our stories correspond.'

Vicky sipped nervously at her coffee and the hot liquid scalded her throat. 'I presume you have thought of something?' she croaked.

'As far as Sam and Hilary are concerned, you can leave it to me,' he instructed. 'To others we can say that we met each other six months ago when I was here in Cape Town on business, that we wrote to each other regularly and, after meeting again on this occasion decided to get married.'

'Were you in Cape Town six months ago?' Vicky asked, sending him a furtive glance.

'Yes.' There was a flicker of amusement in his eyes. 'I think there are a few things we should find out about each other before we try convincing our friends and relatives. Don't you?'

'I ... suppose so.'

Her obvious reluctance appeared to increase his amusement. 'Tell me about your parents.'

Vicky swallowed hard. 'My father was killed in a mine accident in Johannesburg when I was ten. My mother died here in Cape Town two years ago.'

Conrad's expression sobered. 'I'm sorry. I didn't mean to upset you.'

Vicky traced an idle finger along the patterns on the tablecloth. 'It doesn't matter.'

'Is there no one else except Michael and yourself?'

'No one.'

There was a brief silence during which he regarded her intently. 'How old are you, Vicky?'

She lowered her glance. 'Twenty-six.'

'That makes me twelve years your senior,' he observed. So he was thirty-eight, she registered. 'Have you always worked for the same firm?'

'Yes. I started as a junior in the typing pool and worked my way up into the position of private secretary to one of the chief architects.'

There was a hint of pride in her voice and for several minutes a brooding silence settled between them. Vicky, normally a very orderly person, hated the idea of being up-rooted from the familiar routine she had become so accustomed to through the years. She was on the brink of being plunged into a life she knew nothing about; a life that was uncertain, and which included marriage to the stranger seated opposite her. Oh, why had she agreed to it all? she asked herself anxiously.

Conrad emptied his cup and his hand went automatically to the pocket of his overcoat where she had seen him place his pipe, but he changed his mind suddenly and leaned his elbows on the table, his expression faintly amused.

'Aren't you going to ask me about myself?'

Vicky shook off her troubled thoughts. 'Perhaps you should tell me what you think I ought to know,' she replied guardedly.

'All right. My full name is Conrad Stephanus Lodewickus de Jongh,' he began, and Vicky found it impossible to suppress the giggle that burst her lips. 'Did I say something funny?' he asked then, the flicker of amusement still lurking in his eyes.

'Not really,' she replied evasively, endeavouring to control her features. She could not help thinking that he was

28

certainly big enough to carry the load of those three names.

'I was named after my grandfather,' he informed her austerely, but Vicky had observed the slight twitch to those firm lips, indicating that he understood her source of amusement and was not angered.

'Was your grandfather also a big man?' she asked tentatively, her eyes flicking over the wide expanse of shoulders with the proud head resting on a strong, sinewy neck.

'All the men in the de Jongh family are big, and the women are small.'

'Why is this?'

Conrad shrugged his broad shoulders, and the heavy overcoat accentuated their breadth. 'The men in the de Jongh family all married small women. Perhaps their smallness evoked a feeling of protectiveness in the men. I'm not sure.' His eyes were narrowed as he studied her intently, taking in her neat tailored suit, the dampness of her fair hair, and the steady regard of brown eyes that appeared almost luminous in the soft light. 'You're small,' he added almost thoughtfully.

Vicky blushed. 'My size is not significant, for our marriage is merely a business arrangement.'

'Quite true. Our marriage is merely a business arrangement,' he echoed brusquely. 'After the year is up and if neither of us feels inclined to continue with the marriage, I might end up acting quite contrary to all the other de Jongh men by marrying a tall, robust woman who will be quite capable of taking care of herself in such a way that I shan't have to continually worry about her safety as my forefathers had to worry about their wives.'

Vicky glanced up at him sharply, aware of an uneasy stirring beneath the surface of her emotions. Conrad's glance chilled her suddenly and she wondered for a moment if it would not have been better to look for help elsewhere. But where? she wondered dismally.

Conrad must have noticed her troubled expression, for a smile curved his lips, but it did not quite reach his eyes.

'Shall I continue telling you about myself?' he asked, and as Vicky nodded, he continued, 'Since my father's retirement six years ago, I've been farming alone on Duiwelspoort. That's the name of the farm, incidentally,' he added drily.

'Duiwelspoort,' Vicky murmured. Rather a strange name for a farm, she thought. Devil's gateway! Did the de Jongh men perhaps have a devilish streak in their natures? she wondered momentarily, shivering at the thought.

It was almost uncanny the way Conrad sensed her thoughts. 'The name Duiwelspoort is rather misleading,' he explained. 'There's quite a story attached to it, but we haven't time now for lengthy explanations. What else is there that you wish to know?'

His voice sounded so abrupt that for a moment Vicky hesitated before asking, 'Do your parents live on the farm with you?'

'When my father retired he bought a house in George where they now live,' Conrad informed her. 'After six years my father can't quite dissociate himself from the farm and occasionally, around Christmas and Easter, they pay me a visit.'

'How do you think they will react to the news that you —that we——' Vicky stumbled over the words, very conscious of his eyes upon her.

'They're very happy to know that I've at last decided to take the plunge,' he said easily.

Vicky swallowed nervously. 'You've told them already?'

'Yes. They will be here for the wedding ceremony.'

'And when they discover that it's not a real marriage?'

Conrad's eyes narrowed instantly. 'They must not discover the truth. I must ask you to please act as convincingly as you can in their presence.'

'You're asking rather a lot,' Vicky protested agitatedly.

'Do you want to back out?'

The silence was heavily charged as they sat facing each other across the table, and then Vicky shook her head. 'You know it's too late for me to do that.'

Conrad glanced over his shoulder. 'It has stopped raining for the moment. I think it's time I drove you to your flat so that I can have a chat to your brother.'

He told her more about himself while they drove back to the city. 'I have a sister who is married to a farmer in the Transvaal. They have two children, a boy and a girl. My sister's name is Barbara, by the way.'

'Is she older or younger than you?'

'Younger by three years.'

Knowing that his farm was in the Karroo, she said: 'I presume you're a sheep farmer?'

'Yes, that's right,' he smiled at her slightly. 'I also keep about thirty head of cattle, mainly for milking purposes. My mother used to keep a few fowls as a hobby; now the servants have to take care of them, for I haven't the time.'

Vicky sat staring thoughtfully ahead of her, her brow puckered into a frown. Her thoughts were disturbing, and she viewed the future with apprehension. She glanced at Conrad's stern profile and wondered if he, too, felt as uncertain about everything as she did. After all, she was just as much a stranger to him as he was to her. The only difference was that he was returning to a life he knew and loved, while she ... Vicky caught her lower lip between her teeth to steady it.

'Conrad,' she began hesitantly, her hands clenched tightly in her lap. 'Have you realised that I know absolutely nothing about life on a farm?'

He refrained from replying until he had parked the Holden at the entrance to her flat. Then he turned to her, his steel-grey eyes fixed upon her own.

'I could say, wait and see,' he observed, 'but that wouldn't be fair, would it?'

Vicky took a deep breath as Conrad leaned towards her. His nearness was even more disturbing than her thoughts had been a moment ago.

'Conrad, I've lived all my life in a city and I admit that I'm totally ignorant about life on a farm. Tell me about it before we go up to my flat. What does the farm look like? And the house ... is it big or small? Tell me everything, please?'

Conrad's expression altered suddenly. The square jaw jutted out firmly and the chiselled lips appeared less harsh. His grey eyes glanced past her as if he were staring at something he cherished.

'Duiwelspoort is in the Koelenberg district, which is in the heart of the Karroo. When we have a good rainfall the veld is transformed into a carpet of wild flowers and it stretches as far as the eye can see. Aloes grow wild in the veld in among the thorn trees and pepper trees. The house is eight kilometres from the road and one has to drive through the grazing paddocks to reach it. Close to the house there's a stone archway, and from there one drives through an avenue of bluegum trees to reach the house.'

'The house? What does the house look like?' she asked eagerly.

Conrad glanced at her then and smiled. 'You will have to wait until we're there to see what it looks like. I have a generating plant on the farm that supplies us with electricity, and there's water laid on to the house for general and sewerage purposes. There's nothing primitive about my home on Duiwelspoort, if that's what you're afraid of.'

Vicky met his glance unwaveringly. 'I hope you know what you're doing, Conrad. You're taking Michael—who is used to the pleasures a city life can offer, with nothing more

32

strenuous to do than pushing a pen across paper—and you are going to introduce him to a rigorous farm life he knows nothing about. I'm not much better than he is, I can assure you.'

Conrad's lips tightened into a thin, hard line. 'You will both just have to try to adapt yourselves then, won't you?'

One glance at his face was enough to give Vicky a foretaste of what their life would be like in the future. Conrad would be absolutely merciless towards Michael, as well as herself, in the process of claiming repayment. Vicky realised that had she not been so proud she could have approached any one of her friends for help, but the frantic desire to keep Michael's name unblemished in the eyes of these people, whose friendship she valued, had forced her to take a step she would never have dreamed of under normal circumstances. The future had become a frightening monster looming ahead of her along the only path available, and as it stretched out its arms to grasp her she shuddered involuntarily.

'The prospect of living on a farm doesn't appeal to you, does it?' Conrad asked coldly, incorrectly interpreting her involuntary reaction. 'Perhaps the thought that it will only be for a year will be of some consolation to you.'

An awkward silence had settled between them and it was almost a relief to be met by Michael, smiling and relaxed after the tension of the past two days. Slightly built and not very tall, he looked almost pathetically young with his boyish face. If he had realised at that moment what Conrad de Jongh had in mind for him, his welcoming smile would have lost its spontaneity.

Vicky suppressed the desire to weep and turned instead to lead the way to the small lounge with its old but comfortable furniture.

'Vicky telephoned me to give me the news,' Michael

began, and then proceeded to thank Conrad, only to be brusquely interrupted.

'When you've heard what I have to tell you, you may not feel like thanking me. First of all you should know that Vicky and I are to be married the day after tomorrow. Your escapade has naturally hastened this joyous occasion.'

It all came out so glibly that Vicky could only stare at him dumbly as he continued to tell Michael exactly what would be expected of him in the future.

'But, Mr de Jongh ... er ... Conrad,' Michael objected. 'Don't you think you're taking matters a bit too far? I appreciate your financial help, believe me, but surely I could repay you in some other way. I mean ... well ...'

Conrad's glance was flint-hard. 'Exactly how do you propose to repay me?'

'Well, I——'

'You haven't got a job, and neither are you likely to get one soon,' Conrad interrupted brutally. 'The Atlas Company definitely won't be giving you a good recommendation. Without that recommendation any prospective employer will be quite at liberty to contact your previous employer, and it won't take more than a few minutes to discover exactly why you had to leave the Atlas Company in such a hurry.'

'Conrad!' Vicky protested as Michael flinched. 'Is it necessary to be so harsh?'

'My dear,' Conrad began patiently, 'Michael will have to face this fact sooner or later, and the sooner he does so, the better. I'm giving him the opportunity to repay his debt by taking him into my employment. After the debt is cleared off he will have a recommendation in his pocket with which to get another job.'

Michael lit a cigarette with trembling fingers and puffed at it angrily. 'I know absolutely nothing about farming.'

'Then you'll have to learn the hard way,' Conrad retorted quite firmly.

It is very easy mapping out a plan of action, but things do not always work out exactly as you had hoped, and somewhere, someone is going to do the unpredictable and suddenly you find that your carefully planned strategy is useless, Vicky realised. Michael and Conrad had both risen to their feet and as they stood facing each other Vicky glanced nervously from one to the other. Michael was openly defiant and quite unafraid, while Conrad, almost twice Michael's size, registered grim determination on his hard face.

'You can forget the whole idea. I'm not going!' Michael's voice rang out angrily.

For endless seconds an explosive silence hovered in the room. Conrad clenched and unclenched his big hands and for one terrifying second Vicky thought that he was going to hit Michael.

'I'm afraid you have no choice,' she said quickly, hoping to divert Conrad's attention and to relieve the tension.

Michael swung round to face her, a scowl on his face. 'What do you mean, I have no choice?'

Vicky felt trapped. What explanation could she give that would not reveal the true reason for her marriage to Conrad? She glanced up at Conrad helplessly and he immediately rose to the occasion.

'What Vicky is trying to say is that either you agree to work for me on my farm, or I cancel the payment of that cheque I gave to the Atlas Company, which means that the case against you can be reopened.'

Michael paled visibly. 'You wouldn't do that!'

'Wouldn't I?' Michael wilted suddenly beneath Conrad's forceful gaze. 'I presume you would prefer working on the farm to spending some time in prison?'

That final remark broke through the remaining fragments

of Michael's defiance and Vicky sighed with relief when she saw him sink into his chair, nodding wordlessly.

'Have you contacted the agents about your flat?' Conrad asked, turning sharply to Vicky.

She passed the tip of her tongue along her dry lips. 'Yes.'

Conrad nodded approvingly and left soon afterwards, refusing Vicky's offer to stay to dinner. His departing words were: 'You have a lot of packing to do. I suggest you get started.'

Neither Vicky nor Michael discussed the subject again. In sombre silence they ate the meal Vicky had prepared and after the dishes were washed and stacked away, she began to sort through her belongings, deciding which to take with her and which could be stored somewhere until a later date.

During the course of the following day Conrad telephoned Vicky at work to tell her that he had made the necessary application for their marriage to take place the day after, and this somehow put the seal of reality on her nightmare. When she left the office for the last time that afternoon to return home, she found Conrad waiting outside for her in his station-wagon. They collected Michael at the flat and drove to Conrad's hotel to have dinner.

It was to be a celebration dinner, but despite the champagne Conrad had ordered, it was a rather solemn party seated about the table. Michael's curious glances forced Conrad and Vicky to feign happiness, but their efforts dwindled and the meal was completed in silence.

Conrad drove Michael back to the flat and then whisked Vicky off to see Sam and Hilary. As he parked at their gate Vicky became panic-stricken.

'Conrad, they'll never believe us! What are we going to say?'

Conrad gripped her trembling hands in his. 'Don't say or do anything, just leave it all to me. All you have to do is respond to my endearments and try to look happy.' He laughed suddenly, placing a finger beneath her chin and peering down at her through the darkness. 'You're as pale as a ghost, and for a young woman on the eve of her marriage you look totally unkissed.'

The next instant she was caught up in his embrace and before she could protest his mouth had closed over hers. Her mind reeled at the unexpectedness of it and her heart hammered wildly against her ribs. His hand moved against the back of her head and before she had time to realise his intention he had extracted the pins and her hair came cascading down to her shoulders.

He released her then and her hands went instantly to her hair in an effort to restore the damage.

'You didn't have to k-kiss me like that, and just look what you've done to my hair!'

His hands closed over hers in a painful grip. 'Leave it,' he ordered. 'If they find your appearance strange, they'll certainly have no difficulty in realising that I'm the culprit.'

'You are taking advantage of the situation,' she cried angrily, 'and I think you are despicable.'

'That may be so,' he agreed coldly, releasing her hands, 'but I have something which you needed desperately, and you can't quibble about that.'

Vicky gasped at the implication behind his words. 'That was hitting below the belt,' she told him in a muffled voice.

'It was meant to.'

Vicky stared at him speechlessly for a moment. Would she ever understand this man? she wondered. One minute he seemed gentle and the next you felt the cruel lash of his tongue. It was bewildering, and quite frightening.

'I wish I'd never approached you for help,' she cried in anguish, the tears smarting her eyes. 'I wish I'd gone elsewhere.'

'To whom, for instance?' he asked with infuriating calmness.

'To the Bank, I suppose.'

'Don't be silly. The Bank would have demanded to know the reason for the loan, and that would have been the end of that.' He paused slightly. 'Whom else?'

'I could have asked Sam,' Vicky replied, no longer sure of herself.

'Sam has recently put almost every cent he owned into a new business venture,' Conrad remarked. 'Anyone else?'

Vicky wished that she had had the nerve to slap that self-confident look off his face. Conrad de Jongh was infuriating, and what she found even more infuriating was the fact that he had spoken the truth. There *was* no one else who could have helped her, and he knew it.

'You win,' she replied hoarsely. 'There isn't anyone else.'

'Good,' he remarked briefly before helping her out of the Holden. 'We've at least overcome the first obstacle in our relationship.'

To say that Sam and Hilary were astounded by their news would be quite an understatement. Sam looked more than sceptical and Hilary simply laughed as though it was nothing more than a hilarious joke. When Conrad assured them that he had filled in the necessary forms at the magistrate's office, however, their expressions sobered considerably.

'But this is ridiculous,' Hilary spluttered. 'You only met each other two days ago.'

'That's of no consequence to us,' Conrad remarked a trifle drily.

'Oh, very well,' Hilary said. 'Perhaps I can accept the fact that a man like yourself, who's remained a bachelor for so many years, could fall like a ton of bricks for a woman.' She turned, and Vicky received the full impact of her searching gaze. 'But I can't understand you, Vicky. You've never done an impulsive thing in your whole life, and here you

38

are rushing headlong into marriage.' She shook her head. 'It doesn't make sense.'

Vicky was conscious of Conrad's arm about her shoulders. She felt the warm pressure of his fingers increase as he gazed down at her.

'I must say that our friends have overwhelmed us with their congratulations,' he remarked easily, surprising her by dropping a light kiss on her hair.

Sam, who had maintained a thoughtful silence throughout their verbal altercation, removed his pipe from his mouth. 'You must forgive us, Conrad, if we've appeared lacking in manners. Your news caught us unawares, but we would like to congratulate you both, and wish you all the happiness you could wish yourself.'

Hilary regained her composure as the two men shook hands. From seemingly nowhere she produced a bottle of champagne and from that moment on the party became more relaxed. Vicky found herself responding quite naturally to Conrad's gentle approaches. It was of course all done for Sam and Hilary's benefit, Vicky told herself, but the unfamiliar glitter in Conrad's eyes left her strangely weak.

'What are you going to do about your furniture?' Hilary asked somewhere during the proceedings.

'Sell it, I suppose,' Vicky replied vaguely.

'If you like,' Sam offered unexpectedly, 'I'll arrange to have it collected and also do the selling for you, or you might end up getting nothing at all. You know what second-hand dealers are like, always out to get something cheap which can be re-sold at a fantastic profit.'

Vicky agreed instantly and with a certain amount of relief. Though her money had not after all been needed for Michael's bail, there had been a few outstanding accounts of her own, and more of his, that she had felt bound to settle before leaving Cape Town. Also she was feminine enough to treat herself to a few new clothes, though this

39

marriage was not the kind to call for a proper trousseau. So her bank balance was somewhat depleted.

When Conrad drove Vicky home later that evening, she was quite lightheaded with the unaccustomed amount of champagne she had consumed. In the shadows of her doorway, where the prying eyes of the neighbours could not detect them, Conrad swept her into his arms and kissed her passionately, and Vicky was too weak to resist. Later, after a hot bath and a strong cup of coffee, shame and humiliation drove her to tears, and for the first time in many years she cried herself to sleep.

CHAPTER THREE

It had rained during the night and it continued to do so until the early morning. By the time Sam and Hilary arrived to take Michael and Vicky to the magistrate's offices, the rain had mercifully stopped, but the clouds still hung heavily in the sky.

Vicky was tight-lipped and silent as they drove towards the centre of the city. She had always imagined that her wedding day would be the happiest day of her life, the day when, wearing the white dress and veil of her dreams, she would become the wife of the man she loved. Instead, she was heading for a simple ceremony in the magistrate's offices, dressed in a plain, pale blue suit, to marry a man she hardly knew in order to save her brother from going to prison.

The thought was abhorrent and every nerve in her body vibrated tensely. Her mood matched the sombre clouds in the sky until she caught Michael's anxious glance resting on her face. If only for his sake, she had to fake happiness.

'You're not nervous, are you?' Sam asked, glancing at her in the rear view mirror.

'Of course she's nervous!' Hilary cut in sharply before Vicky could reply. 'Wasn't I terrified with happiness on our wedding day?'

Sam snorted loudly and Vicky's lips twisted into an involuntary smile as she met his exasperated expression in the mirror.

'No one else but you could be terrified with happiness,' Sam said at length, glancing at his wife affectionately.

'You're the only one I know of who could combine two such contrasting emotions, and yet make sense.'

Conrad and his parents, Anton and Elinor de Jongh, were waiting outside when they arrived, but fortunately there was barely time to introduce Vicky before they had to enter the building.

Conrad stood tall and immaculate in his dark suit beside Vicky and she was aware of the fact that her head barely reached his heart. Conrad's father was equally tall and well-built for his age, and between the two of them they dwarfed the rest of the entourage.

Her hand trembled as it rested on his arm and for a brief moment his fingers closed firmly about hers in a warm, reassuring clasp. Did he sense her nervousness and the turmoil her emotions were in? Or was he merely acting in the way expected of him?

The wedding ceremony was brief, and when Conrad finally slipped the plain gold wedding band on to her finger, her emotions got the better of her and she had to catch her trembling lip between her teeth to steady it. Her glance was drawn to Conrad's and his expression disturbed her and filled her with unaccustomed panic. She had the uncomfortable feeling that she was like a fly trapped in a web from which there was no escape.

The officiating magistrate indicated that the groom might kiss the bride, and Conrad obliged by kissing her long and hard while she remained standing stiffly in his embrace. He had to do this, Vicky realised, for the sake of the family and friends present, and everything had to appear as normal as possible. Victoria Reid was now legally Victoria de Jongh, and it seemed strange that such an impersonal ceremony could bring about this change.

'May I kiss the bride?' Sam asked laughingly and, without waiting for Conrad to reply, he embraced Vicky and bestowed a friendly kiss upon her lips. He pinched her pale cheek. 'Getting married is a nerve-racking affair, but you can relax now. It's over.'

It's over! Yes, it was all over, and there was no turning back.

Hilary was tearful as she hugged both Vicky and Conrad, and Michael, too, seemed to find his voice with difficulty, which almost succeeded in reducing Vicky to tears.

There was, again, no time for Conrad's parents to speak privately with Vicky, for Conrad wanted to leave as soon as possible.

'We're so happy for you both,' they said, embracing their son and then Vicky.

Elinor de Jongh drew Vicky to one side. 'My only regret is that there has been no time to get to know you but, knowing Conrad, I'm sure he has made a wise choice.'

Vicky's heart was won over instantly and she looked forward to meeting her, as well as Conrad's father, at a later date after she had been afforded the opportunity of becoming more settled in her new way of life.

Conrad became impatient. 'We have a long drive ahead of us and the sooner we leave, the better,' he explained, and Vicky's heart became a lead weight in her chest.

The dirt road lay endlessly ahead of them, twisting and turning among the occasional flat-topped hills. They had long since left the Cape behind them where the towering peaks of the Dutoits mountain range had taken her breath away, and the acres of brilliantly coloured vineyards had saddened her as they shed their autumn finery.

They had turned off the main road several kilometres back and were travelling deeper into the Karroo, a vast scrub-covered land, with nothing but the occasional appearance of acacia and pepper trees to break the monotony. The Holden held the road firmly, throwing up a cloud of dust behind it while the rhythmic hum of the engine made

Vicky drowsy. Beneath drooping eyelids she caught the gleam of gold on her left hand, and she sat for endless seconds staring at the thin gold band on her finger. It felt unfamiliar and more than a little frightening.

No one had spoken much on the journey from Cape Town. Michael had remained sullenly silent in the back of the Holden and Conrad, too, had maintained a brooding silence as he drove steadily towards Koelenberg. The skies were clear in the Karroo and the warmth of the sun stole through Vicky's shivering form until she felt relaxed and pleasantly drowsy.

After they had stopped for lunch, Conrad and Michael had both discarded their jackets and loosened their ties before continuing their journey. Lying with her head back against the seat, Vicky could observe Conrad unobtrusively, allowing her glance to linger on the dark head with the smattering of grey at the temples, the hard, sometimes cruel face, and the massive shoulders with the white shirt spanning across the breadth of them. He had rolled up his shirt sleeves to above his elbows, and with every movement the muscles in his forearm rippled, while the broad hands resting on the steering wheel gave the appearance of being in complete control.

'Have we still far to go?' Vicky asked curiously, breaking the comfortable silence.

'Another two hours' travelling.' Conrad glanced down at her quickly. 'You might as well try to sleep for a while. This road is rather monotonous.'

'Will you wake me just before we reach Koelenberg?'

Conrad nodded briefly and Vicky's eyelids drooped until her eyelashes lay fanned across her cheeks. For the first time in three days, Vicky slept soundly and dreamlessly, and she would have continued to do so had she not eventually become aware of a hand moving against her cheek. She opened her eyes lazily and looked straight into Conrad's grey eyes and then, to her embarrassment, discovered that she had slid sideways in her sleep and had been using his shoulder as a pillow.

'I'm terribly sorry,' she muttered, moving away from him quickly and blushing scarlet. 'I didn't realise that I was propping myself up against you.'

'Don't let it trouble you.' He released the clutch and the Holden moved forward, gaining speed. 'Koelenberg is just ahead of us.'

The rooftops of houses were visible in the distance, and it was with a certain amount of anxiety that Vicky realised they were nearing the end of their journey, and approaching the beginning of a new life that filled her with trepidation. She turned in her seat to speak to Michael only to discover that he, too, had fallen asleep.

'Don't wake him,' Conrad ordered softly beside her. 'His life will be drastically altered as from tomorrow, so let him sleep while he has the opportunity.'

Vicky could not be sure if he was merely being kind, or whether there was an underlying threat in his softly spoken words. Conrad's granite-hard expression certainly gave her no indication of what he was actually thinking at that moment.

There was no time, however, to ponder this question, for Conrad reduced speed as they entered Koelenberg and Vicky looked about her with interest. This was the town she would no doubt be frequenting during her stay at Duiwelspoort, and she might as well become acquainted with what it had to offer, she decided firmly.

It was a beautiful town, she had to admit. It appeared as though time had stood still in Koelenberg, for it looked completely untouched by progress. The shops were old, but quaint, with their fancy wrought-iron work on zinc awnings. The streets were broad and lined with, strangely enough, tall pear trees.

'Do they actually bear fruit?' Vicky asked in astonishment.

'They do, but the trees are so tall that picking the fruit is more trouble than it's worth.' Conrad smiled suddenly. 'The children are usually enterprising enough to climb the trees to pick those within their reach.'

'Did you do that as a child?' she asked suspiciously, unable to imagine him as a carefree child climbing trees like all the other boys.

'Would it shock you if I told you that I did?'

'It's the most natural thing for boys to climb trees,' Vicky evaded his question.

'But you can't imagine me doing that,' he supposed correctly, parking the Holden at the entrance to an old stone building and turning to her with a look of scorn on his face. 'I can assure you that I was a very normal child, just as you will discover that I am a very normal man.' Conrad stepped out of the car and slammed the door with unnecessary force. 'I'm going to collect my post.'

'Don't tell me you've had your first argument?' a sleepy voice asked from behind her.

Vicky spun round in her seat. 'Are you awake?'

'Conrad slammed the door so hard I couldn't help waking,' Michael grunted, pushing his fingers through his hair and yawning. 'Were you arguing about something?'

'Don't be silly,' Vicky replied, turning away from him to hide her expression. She and Conrad had not been arguing, yet Conrad's remark had left her feeling strangely disturbed.

For the first time Vicky took stock of the situation. What did she really know about Conrad de Jongh other than that he was an old friend of Sam's, and that he farmed on Duiwelspoort? The other snippets of information had not really given her a clear insight into his character, and the thought that unnerved her most was that she had agreed so

46

readily to marry him. An alarming thought flashed through her mind. Why had he been so insistent that she should marry him? Despite the fact that he had stipulated that their marriage would be in name only, was he perhaps planning to reap payment from her as well? If not in cash, then in kind? It was a tantalising question that set her nerves on edge as the full implication of her actions became clear to her.

Vicky was thoroughly unnerved by the time Conrad returned to the Holden and slid behind the wheel. He was obviously in a hurry now to get to Duiwelspoort and fortunately gave her nothing more than a cursory glance or he, too, might have been unnerved by the alarm registered clearly in her eyes.

'Duiwelspoort is not far now,' Conrad remarked conversationally, unaware that Vicky was regarding him with new eyes. Eyes that expressed fear and uncertainty. 'There is one important fact I must impress upon both of you,' he continued. 'Don't leave any gates open. An open gate could mean severe loss.'

What possible loss could an open gate cause? Vicky thought irritably, but tactfully refrained from voicing her doubts. She glanced instead at the sheep grazing in the veld and tried to steady her scattered thoughts by counting them, an impossible task, she realised after only a few minutes. How on earth was a sheep farmer able to count his livestock in order to know whether there were any missing? she wondered bemusedly as Conrad swung the Holden off the road.

On a notice board, attached to the gate, were printed the words 'C.S.L. de Jongh—Duiwelspoort', and unaccustomed anxiety seemed to twist her stomach muscles into a knot.

'We're home,' Conrad remarked unnecessarily while Michael opened the gate and stood waiting for them to

47

drive through. 'Welcome to Duiwelspoort, Mrs de Jongh.'

Vicky's lips moved, but no sound came. It was moments later she realised she had been rendered speechless while in the grip of sheer terror.

'We're home,' Conrad had said, and Vicky had shuddered. How could this semi-desert, scrub-covered country ever become her home? *Mrs de Jongh*, he had called her. Was she really Mrs Conrad de Jongh? What on earth had possessed her to agree so easily with his plans? she kept wondering frantically. Had the horror of Michael's foolishness slightly deranged her?

They went through several gates, how many Vicky could not tell afterwards. She regained control of her emotions as the stone archway Conrad had mentioned loomed up ahead. They drove through it and Vicky became pleasantly aware of spacious lawns with neatly trimmed privet hedges, while the rose garden yielded a crop of late autumn roses. Ornamental shrubs had been planted with great foresight and were obviously lovingly cared for. Large trees created shady corners where garden benches had been strategically placed, affording the garden an air of peace and tranquillity which Vicky could not appreciate at that moment.

The house was strikingly beautiful as it stood against the background of tall poplar trees. Double-storied with large windows and trellised stoep running along the front and both sides of the house, it obviously dated back a hundred years or more, but there was no sign of neglect as Vicky's glance swept appreciatively over it.

The Holden crunched to a halt at the front entrance and Vicky slipped out quickly to take a closer look at her new surroundings while Conrad and Michael alighted more slowly. One would have to be dull-witted not to notice the charm and beauty of this old homestead which had housed nearly three generations of de Jonghs, Vicky thought, sighing ecstatically as she glanced at the ivy creeper trailing up the trellis along one side of the stoep to protect the potted ferns from the devastating rays of the sun.

For some unknown reason Michael's scowling face angered her at that moment and she turned away from him quickly to see Conrad leaning against the Holden, his arms folded across his broad chest and his head slightly tilted as he regarded her.

'Well?' he said, and Vicky sensed that behind that one word lay far more than just an inquiry. Conrad wanted her to like his home, and his anxiety was growing as the seconds ticked by.

Vicky spread out her arms as if to include not only the house but the grounds as well. 'It's beautiful,' she said simply, meeting his glance unwaveringly. 'I'm glad that you left it as a surprise.'

There was an odd expression in Conrad's eyes which was wholly disconcerting and Vicky's pulse rate quickened alarmingly as she found herself unable to tear her glance away from his.

'I could do with something to drink,' Michael remarked impatiently.

Conrad glanced at him then, his expression cold, his lips drawn into a thin line of disapproval. For a brief moment Vicky thought that Conrad was about to rebuke him, but the next moment his facial muscles relaxed as he eased himself away from the Holden.

'We can all do with something to drink,' he said briefly. 'Let's get these suitcases inside first.'

Despite Conrad's protests Vicky insisted on helping and, laden with suitcases, they had barely mounted the steps when the sound of a horse's hooves made all three of them turn.

A chestnut mare came galloping up the drive towards them and on its back sat the most beautiful girl Vicky had ever seen, her body moving gracefully to match the rhythm

49

of the mare's movements beneath her. At the foot of the steps she slid to the ground and hurried towards them while the mare quivered slightly from the exertion and then stood perfectly still.

At close range the girl was even more beautiful than Vicky had thought, with black hair, almost as black as Conrad's, hanging straight down to her shoulders and carelessly tucked in behind shell-shaped ears. Startlingly clear blue eyes were at that moment fixed possessively on Conrad, and red lips parted in a smile that displayed small, beautifully shaped teeth. Her jodhpurs were immaculate and her blouse a crisp white.

Vick glanced down at her own linen suit with a rueful expression as she noted the creases caused by the long hours of having to remain seated in the Holden, and even worse, she knew her nose was shining.

The girl took the last two steps in one stride and flung herself upon Conrad, her arms fastening about his neck as she pulled his head down and kissed him passionately, or so it seemed to Vicky, who stood beside him watching this exuberant display of affection.

'Darling, I've missed you terribly!' she exclaimed, her voice husky and quite unconsciously seductive. 'When I saw the Holden ploughing through the veld I just had to come at once.'

Conrad cleared his throat and loosened her arms from about his neck in order to straighten himself once more to his normal height.

'Natalie,' he began, glancing at the two stunned and silent people beside him, 'I would like you to meet my wife, Vicky, and her brother, Michael Reid.'

The girl's face assumed a mask of utter incredulity as her glance swept from Vicky to Michael and then back to Conrad once more.

'Your *what*?'

'My wife,' Conrad repeated calmly, and as if to stress the fact he placed an arm about Vicky and pulled her hard against his side. 'Vicky, this is Natalie van Buuren. Her parents own the farm adjoining Duiwelspoort.'

Natalie appeared to regain her voice. 'But you never said——'

'Have I ever discussed my personal affairs with you?' Conrad interrupted, maintaining an outward calm although Vicky could feel the impatience in the tenseness of his hard body against her own.

'No, but——' She stopped, obviously unable to continue. Her glance swept deliberately over Vicky, taking in her appearance and weighing it up against her own. Her glance went to Michael, who stared at her almost open-mouthed.

Vicky, acutely conscious of Conrad's arm about her waist and the long, hard line of his body pressed against her own, saw Natalie say something to Michael to which he replied, but the sound of their voices was drowned by the drumming of her pulse against her temples.

'If you don't mind, Natalie,' Conrad's voice filtered through to Vicky, 'we've just arrived and we're tired and hungry.'

'Oh, very well,' the girl acknowledged, skipping down the steps and mounting her horse. 'Mother told me to invite you to dinner tomorrow evening.' Her glance swept over Vicky and Michael once more. 'I suppose we shall have to extend the invitation to all three of you now,' she added ungraciously.

Conrad's arm tightened about Vicky as she trembled with anger. Who the devil did the girl think she was to speak of them so condescendingly? she wondered furiously.

'My wife,' Conrad almost stressed the word, 'and her brother need time to settle down. Perhaps we shall accept your mother's kind invitation to dinner at a later date. If

51

you explain the circumstances to her I'm sure she will understand.'

'I suppose so,' came the disgruntled reply. The chestnut mare was becoming impatient under the tight hold Natalie had on the reins.

'You're forgetting your manners,' Conrad remarked coolly.

The girl had the grace to blush then. 'Oh, yes. Congratulations.' She lifted her head proudly as, with a tug at the reins, she turned the mare about and rider and horse disappeared down the drive as swiftly as they had arrived.

Vicky glanced up at Conrad and her heart lurched at his tight-lipped expression. An idea took shape in her mind which, as she was later to discover, she would find difficult to relinquish. Could Conrad be in love with Natalie van Buuren, and if this was so, then why had he insisted on Vicky's marrying him? Natalie was obviously still very young; she could not possibly be more than nineteen, Vicky decided thoughtfully.

The heavy oak door opened behind them and Vicky shelved the matter, dismissing it as absurd as they turned to face the Coloured woman who had appeared in the doorway.

'I'm so glad the Master has come,' she said excitedly, a smile lighting up her face. 'And the Master has brought the Madam and her brother with him too.' She laughed happily. 'I can't tell the Master how excited Jim and I were when the Master telephoned to say that he was getting married.'

So Conrad had telephoned to say that he was to be married, Vicky thought feverishly. What else had he told them? The truth? The Coloureds were shrewd and not easily fooled, and it would not take this woman long to discover the truth, of that Vicky was certain.

Conrad made the necessary introductions and Lizzie, as

Conrad had said her name was, took the hand Vicky extended towards her and curtsied slightly.

'Madam, it is time there was a woman on Duiwelspoort again,' she announced, 'and I can see now why the Master has waited so long.'

'Oh?' Vicky's glance was puzzled.

'Yes, Madam,' Lizzie continued, helping them in with the suitcases. 'The Madam is not only beautiful, but the Madam is small and fair. The de Jongh men have always married small, fair women.'

Conrad had been the first to mention this fact to her, and now Lizzie had repeated it, adding to it a tremendous compliment. No one had ever called her beautiful before, she thought, blushing painfully as Lizzie's keen eyes took in her appearance.

'Where is Jim?' Conrad asked brusquely, entering the house with the last of their suitcases.

A Coloured man appeared in the doorway behind them as if he were called. 'I am here, Master Conrad.'

'This is Lizzie's husband, Jim,' Conrad informed Vicky as the man bowed respectfully over her hand. 'Lend a hand with the suitcases, Jim,' Conrad instructed, 'and Lizzie, what about making a pot of tea?'

Lizzie chuckled and left them, her blue, starched overall and crisp white apron almost crackling as she moved.

As the three men dispersed with the suitcases, Vicky glanced about her quickly before moving up the stairs behind them.

The hallway was spacious with a grandfather clock standing against one wall. In the one corner stood a hat-stand which contained walking-sticks, several of which had magnificently carved handles, and hanging on a peg just above them was a broad-brimmed safari hat with a leopardskin band around it. Conrad's? she wondered curiously, finding it difficult to imagine him wearing it.

53

Three doors opened into the hallway, but they were all closed and Vicky wondered disappointedly what lay behind them. There was one door immediately to her left and another to her right. To the right of the staircase there was a passage along which another door was kept mysteriously closed, and at the end of the passage was the entrance to the kitchen, judging by the sounds coming from that direction.

Vicky slowly mounted the stairs, trailing her hand lightly on the delicately carved stinkwood balustrade as it curved upwards to the next floor. On the landing she paused a moment to glance at the framed portraits lining the wall. One portrait in particular caught her attention. It was of a woman, small and fair, her hair combed up in a style dating back to the previous century. Her dress was blue and bustled, with lace at her throat and wrists. Whoever she was, Vicky decided, she was undoubtedly beautiful.

'Are you coming?' Conrad asked from above her, his voice edged with impatience.

Vicky glanced up at him swiftly and smiled. 'Coming, Conrad.'

He took her hand as she reached him and led her to the left along the passage. Jim passed them on the way and smiled broadly as Conrad thanked him for his help. Conrad steered Vicky ahead of him into one of the rooms and her breath caught sharply in her throat.

It was a large room with heavy velvet curtaining at the window with a stinkwood chest of drawers beneath it. A large yellowwood wardrobe stood against one wall with a full-length mirror fastened to the wall beside it. The dressing-table was of beautiful carved ebony wood with a smaller mirror above it, and beside it stood a stinkwood chair with its seat made of fine leather strips.

All this Vicky noticed at a swift glance, for her eyes, large and frightened, were riveted to the enormous four-poster bed with its silk drapes and matching bedspread reaching down to the carpeted floor.

Conrad's hands came down on her shoulders and she stiffened instantly as she felt the warmth of his body behind her.

'This will be your room,' he pointed out, and his voice, deep and calm, had a soothing effect on her shattered nerves. 'The bathroom is through here,' he waved his hand towards a door leading off the room and Vicky wandered in that direction.

She was surprised to discover that the bathroom was beautifully tiled and modern, in contrast with the room she had just left. There was just one other matter that bothered her, and she questioned Conrad about it when she returned to the room.

'That door,' she began, pointing to the other end of the room. 'Where does it lead to?'

A flicker of a smile crossed his face. 'That is normally used as a dressing-room,' he informed her. 'It also has a private entrance into the passage. Come, I will show you.'

Vicky found herself almost unwillingly steered in that direction. Conrad flung open the door and Vicky walked in ahead of him a little hesitantly. It was a small room, less than half the size of the one she was to occupy. A yellow-wood wardrobe, an exact replica of the one in her bedroom, stood against one wall, and the only other furniture in the room was a small chest of drawers, a straight-backed chair and a single bed.

'This will be my room,' Conrad said quietly, and Vicky's glance went instantly to the communicating door. There was no key! 'You will have to trust me,' Conrad remarked, sensing her thoughts, his eyes glittering.

Vicky's cheeks were stained pink. 'Where is Michael's room?' she asked over her shoulder, not daring to meet his glance until she had regained her composure.

'His room is down the other end of the passage.'

Down the other end of the passage seemed miles away. Would Michael ever be able to hear if she needed his help? Blushing crimson at her own thoughts, she hastily walked over to the window and stared down into the garden below. It was even more beautiful from that height.

Conrad came up behind her, tall and broad and alarming. He fingered a stray curl in her neck and she trembled at his touch.

'Don't be frightened, Vicky,' he said softly, placing his hands on her shoulders and turning her to face him. His expression was inscrutable as she raised her glance to his.

'I'm not frightened,' she denied, her glance faltering.

'Yes, you are,' he insisted, shaking her slightly. 'You're tense and nervous, and terrified at the thought of what I might do. Admit it!'

The corners of her mouth trembled slightly. 'You say and do things sometimes that frighten me,' she admitted reluctantly.

'I don't recall ever saying anything to frighten you, and the only other thing I have ever done which could possibly have frightened you, is this.'

For the fourth time since she had known him she found herself swept into his arms and thoroughly kissed.

'Was that so frightening?' he asked, not quite relinquishing his hold on her.

'You—you shouldn't kiss me like that,' she gasped breathlessly.

'Oh, come now, Vicky,' he laughed. 'You're twenty-six and you surely don't expect me to believe that you've never been kissed before?'

'I—well—not like that,' she stammered uncomfortably.

'In what way, then?' he demanded.

Vicky tried to free herself. 'Please, Conrad. Let's stop this ridiculous discussion.'

She might have succeeded in escaping him, but he was too quick for her and she found her wrist grasped painfully.

'Show me,' he demanded, and Vicky knew that he would not rest until she had done his bidding. She stood on tiptoe and raised her lips, lightly brushing his own in a fleeting kiss, the colour rising painfully to her cheeks.

Conrad's heavy eyebrows were raised mockingly above eyes that glittered strangely. 'Do you call that a kiss?'

'By the usual standards, yes,' Vicky replied shortly, twisting out of his hold.

'What type of men did you knock about with, then?'

'I did not—knock about with men, as you put it,' she replied indignantly, her brown eyes darkening. 'I occasionally went out with a man if I enjoyed his company.'

'Was there never anyone special?'

'No.'

'Don't you like men?'

Vicky glanced up at him sharply. 'I didn't say that.'

'No, but you're implying it.'

'I'm not implying anything,' she replied hotly. 'All I can say is that I have never yet met a man with whom I've thought I could spend the rest of my life.'

'Do you think you'll recognise the symptoms when you meet your Mr Right?'

'I—I suppose so.'

Vicky wrung her hands nervously together, meticulously avoiding his glance. Would she recognise love when she encountered it? She could not tell. The only thing she was certain of at that moment was that Conrad was the first man to upset her emotionally, and whose presence made her nerves vibrate alarmingly. Why? she wondered. Why did he have this effect on her? Was it fear that made her quiver in his presence like an animal sensing danger?

'If you would like to freshen up a bit, you can do so,'

Conrad interrupted her thoughts. 'When you are ready, come downstairs to the living-room. Tea will be waiting.'

Without waiting for a reply he turned on his heel and left the room, leaving Vicky with the peculiar feeling that she had been dropped on a desert island and left to her own devices.

Don't be ridiculous, she reprimanded herself, and strode purposefully towards her suitcases which were placed neatly at the foot of the bed. She opened one and selected a lemon-coloured dress which had miraculously remained uncreased for the duration of their journey, and with this over her arm she quickly went through to the bathroom.

Some time later, looking cool and refreshed with her corn-coloured hair neatly combed into a roll at the back of her head, she left the bedroom and wandered downstairs, pausing only briefly this time at the portrait she had admired on her arrival.

One of the doors opening into the hallway stood open, Vicky noticed, and judging from the sound of voices and rattling tea-cups, it had to be the living-room. Conrad was standing at the window with a cup of tea in his hands when she entered, while Michael lounged in a chair, also with a cup at his elbow. The air was somehow tense when she entered, and nervously she approached the tea trolley and helped herself to tea and a buttered scone.

'Feeling better?' Conrad asked, turning away from the window to place his empty cup on the trolley.

'Yes, thank you,' she muttered, sitting down in the nearest chair to take the weight off her trembling legs. She looked about her with interest, and discovered to her surprise that the living-room was tastefully, though sparsely, furnished.

There was a comfortable-looking sofa with four equally comfortable-looking chairs, all with padded arms and back rests, and covered in thick, cream-coloured, corded material. Above the fireplace hung an enormous landscape painting, which was the only ornamentation in the room. The matching curtains at the window were of the same heavy material as those in the bedroom she was to occupy, and small occasional tables stood within easy reach of each chair. Everything was perfect, but it curiously lacked the feminine touch, she thought as she bit into the scone.

She became aware of Conrad standing beside her chair, and tensed instantly. His hand came down on to her shoulder in a light caressing movement. Was this for Michael's benefit? she wondered nervously. 'There are a few things I must see to before the sun sets,' he said, unaware of the peculiar sensations his caressing hand was creating. His glance went sharply to Michael. 'You might as well come along to get your first glimpse of what life on a farm is all about.'

Vicky swallowed at the lump in her throat. Once again she was left alone, but it was not the feeling of being deserted that troubled her on this occasion, it was the effect his caressing hand had on her pulse rate that perturbed her most.

She discovered that evening that Lizzie was an exceptionally good cook and she did not hesitate to compliment her on her achievements. Lizzie grew inches taller with the praise Vicky bestowed upon her, and without realising it, Vicky had acquired a friend for life.

After dinner Vicky did the rest of her unpacking, but when her task was completed the silence in the house drove her downstairs and out on to the stoep. The air was cool and free from the city smog, the silence restful, and the stars more brilliant than she had ever imagined. The only sounds seemed to be the chirruping of the crickets in the undergrowth, and the croaking of the frogs in the distance.

Just then another sound reached her ears. The scraping of a foot on the cement stoep. She turned quickly and in the darkness discerned a large shape leaning against the rail, obviously smoking a pipe, judging by the pleasant odour of tobacco that drifted towards her. Should she go indoors without making her presence known? she wondered nervously. Or would such an action of fleeing only cause him amusement? Some instinct made her walk in his direction without further consideration.

'Conrad?' she whispered his name softly, questioningly.

The dark shape turned swiftly and for a fleeting moment he towered frighteningly above her, then her fear evaporated as if it had never been born.

'Vicky!' His voice was startled and rasping. 'I thought you'd gone to bed.'

'No. I was unpacking.'

She wished suddenly that she could see his expression, but, with only a sliver of moon in the sky, the darkness was thick and mysterious. She did, however, notice the hand that held the pipe move unobtrusively towards his trouser pocket.

'Don't do that!' she begged, and touched his arm with her hand. His skin was warm beneath her fingers, the muscles hard.

The silence that followed was almost electrifying and Vicky hastily removed her hand, thankful that the velvety blackness hid her fiery cheeks.

'I believe women don't usually care for the smell of pipe tobacco,' he said.

'How you must have suffered these past few days,' she remarked with attempted humour.

Conrad moved closer to her, so close, in fact, that she could feel his breath on her forehead. He pushed the pipe into his pocket and took her face between his hands. They were warm and strong and, for some reason, his touch held no fear for her.

She felt his lips brush her forehead lightly. 'It has been a long and tiring day for you, Vicky. I suggest you go to bed and get as much sleep as possible. Tomorrow you shall have all day to explore and become acquainted with your new home, but now you must get some rest.'

He bent his head and brushed his lips against her own. Then he was gone, walking down the steps and away from her until he became enveloped in the darkness.

CHAPTER FOUR

VICKY awoke the following morning to the sound of birds chattering in the trees and with the sun filtering into her room through the lace curtains at the window. For a few startled seconds she had no idea where she was; then, remembering, she threw aside the blankets and bathed and dressed as quickly as she could. Later, while doing her hair and adding a touch of make-up to her face, she glanced at the door joining Conrad's room with her own and wondered curiously what time he had come in the previous evening, and whether he was at that moment still sleeping.

The clock in the hall struck seven-thirty as Vicky ventured in the direction she thought the kitchen to be. The second door leading from the hallway, she had discovered the previous evening, led to the dining-room, but the door which she passed on her way to the kitchen was closed, and what lay behind it was still a mystery to her.

'Good morning, Madam,' Lizzie greeted as Vicky entered the kitchen. 'Did the Madam sleep well?'

'Very well, thank you, Lizzie.' She glanced nervously over her shoulder. 'Has everyone else had breakfast?'

'Yes, Madam. Master Conrad and Master Michael had breakfast an hour ago.' Lizzie smiled at Vicky. 'Would the Madam like something to eat now?'

'Just a slice of toast, thank you.' She took one glance at the black coal stove and decided against offering to make it herself. 'A cup of coffee would be nice too.'

Lizzie uttered a sound that hovered between disgust and amusement. 'The Madam can't just eat one slice of toast!'

'But I never have more than that for breakfast,' Vicky

protested, but eventually capitulated when Lizzie insisted she should have an egg with it.

'I will bring the Madam's breakfast to the dining-room.'

'Nonsense,' Vicky protested, and this time she was adamant. 'I'll have it right here in the kitchen.'

Lizzie laughed suddenly, her eyes lighting up with pleasure. 'Madam!' she exclaimed. 'The Madam is a Madam after my own heart.'

Deftly she cleared the table and before very much longer Vicky was eating her breakfast while Lizzie went about her duties.

'Tell me,' Vicky began when she had cleared the last morsel of egg from her plate, 'have you worked here for many years, Lizzie?'

'Many years, Madam,' Lizzie replied, placing a cup of coffee at Vicky's elbow and removing the empty plate. 'I have been working here since Master Conral was a small boy. I was young then, too, and not married to Jim yet.'

'You know him well, then? Master Conrad, I mean?'

'Ag, yes, Madam. I know Master Conrad very well.'

Vicky lapsed into silence, sipping her coffee while watching with interest as Lizzie stoked the fire.

'How do you manage to cook such delightful food on that monstrous stove?' Vicky wanted to know, pushing her empty cup aside and getting to her feet.

Lizzie smiled self-consciously. 'Master Conrad bought an electric stove last year.' She pointed at the shiny stove at the other end of the kitchen and laughed. 'Twice I burnt the dinner, so Master Conrad said it would be better if I went back to the coal stove because it looked as though he would starve to death before I had time to get used to the new one.'

Vicky could not prevent herself from smiling. The Coloureds had a charming accent and a way of saying things that was unique. Lizzie's 'Master' and 'Madam' sounded more like 'Mahser' and 'Marrim', and she used them so religiously—though quite without servility—that it never failed to amuse Vicky.

'Do you do everything in the house as well as the cooking?' Vicky asked with interest.

'When it was only Master Conrad in the house, I did everything, Madam, but now that the Madam and Master Michael are here my sister's child will be coming in to help me.'

Vicky nodded thoughtfully and stood about a moment longer then, pushing her thumbs into the belt of her slacks, she wandered out through the kitchen door. As if from out of nowhere two enormous Great Danes appeared and they streaked down upon her at heart-stopping speed. With a horrified cry she fell back against the side of the kitchen door, a sharp pain stabbing through her shoulder.

'Caesar! Cleo! Down!'

The shouted command acted like a whiplash and both animals sat down obediently, making little whimpering noises.

Vicky tore her frightened glance from them to see Conrad striding towards her. It was a Conrad she hardly recognised in his heavy boots, khaki trousers, short-sleeved khaki safari jacket, and the hat with the leopardskin band planted rakishly on his head.

Lizzie appeared in the doorway, her eyes wide with fright. 'Don't tell me those dogs attacked you, Madam?' she demanded suspiciously.

'No—no, they didn't,' Vicky replied weakly.

'Are you hurt?' Conrad asked, suddenly towering above her.

'I think—my shoulder,' she stammered, touching it lightly.

'Let's have a look,' he said, and before she could protest he had gripped her other arm and, dropping his hat on the kitchen table, he marched her into the house.

'I always said those brutes might hurt someone one day,' Lizzie's accusation followed them up the stairs.

Conrad took her through her bedroom and into the bathroom, instructing her to sit down on the stool. 'Slip off your blouse.'

'Oh, really, Conrad!' she protested in alarm. 'It's nothing serious.'

To her deep embarrassment he undid the buttons of her blouse, firmly pushing her hands aside when she tried to stop him. He slid her blouse off her shoulder and did the same with the flimsy strap of her bra. If it had not been for the expressionless mask he wore, Vicky would have died of shame at the thought of sitting there before him in that partially undressed state.

For someone with such large hands Conrad was surprisingly gentle as he probed her shoulder to discover the extent of her injury. His touch was disturbing, yet she managed to appear outwardly calm.

'There's no serious damage,' he told her calmly. 'The skin is slightly grazed and there might be a slight discolouration tomorrow. Nothing more.'

Vicky was about to lift her blouse on to her shoulder when his hands restrained her. 'I'd like to put something on it before you do that.'

He left the bathroom and Vicky heard him entering his own room through the communicating door. Moments later he returned with a first-aid box in his hands.

'What are you going to do?' she asked hesitantly, acutely conscious of her partially clad figure.

'Don't look so suspicious.' He unscrewed the cap of a small bottle and soaked a piece of cottonwool in the liquid. 'I merely want to put a lotion on that graze to make it feel more comfortable,' he explained.

He dabbed her shoulder lightly with the cottonwool and

whatever it was he had soaked it with, it was decidedly cool and instantly removed the sting. He left it a moment to dry and then slipped the strap of her bra on to her shoulder and did the same with her blouse.

Vicky flushed deeply beneath his glance and turned her back on him as she fastened the buttons and pushed her blouse into her jeans. When she turned around she found that he had gone, and so also had the first-aid box. Gingerly she moved her arm and shoulder, but she felt no discomfort.

She left the bathroom and moved into the bedroom just as Conrad emerged from his own room.

'Feeling better?' he queried.

'Yes, thank you very much.'

He stood looking at her for a moment, his expression unfathomable. 'I'm sorry you were frightened. They wouldn't really have hurt you. They are still young and playful and rather too boisterous in welcoming people. They are not vicious . . . yet,' he added, grinning slightly.

'It was rather frightening,' she admitted shakily. 'It was so unexpected. If I'd known they weren't,' she smiled, 'vicious, I might not have been so terrified. I'm sorry to have caused so much trouble.'

A brief silence followed. Conrad's glance swept over her. 'Can you ride a horse?' he asked unexpectedly.

'I used to . . . once,' she replied hesitantly. 'Michael rides very well, though.'

'So I discovered this morning,' he remarked drily. 'Would you like to ride?'

'Ride a horse, you mean?' she asked, startled.

'That's what we're talking about, isn't it?' His voice was impatient.

'I would like to very much,' she replied evenly, excitement welling up inside her.

'Then there's no time like the present,' he said briskly. 'Do you feel up to it?'

'Yes. Yes, please,' she said, and then wished fervently that she had not sounded so eager.

The stables were just beyond the row of poplar trees, and, breathless from the exertion of keeping pace with Conrad's long strides, Vicky stood waiting nervously while he selected a mount for her.

'You never told me that you had horses on the farm,' she remarked as he saddled a beautiful brown mare with a glistening coat.

'It's much easier to get about on horseback when you're rounding up sheep,' he replied, tightening the stirrup leather.

'What's her name?' she asked, timidly stroking the mare's nose.

'Teresa.'

Vicky's eyes widened as she saw a big black stallion being led from the stable by a coloured boy. It was the most beautiful horse she had ever seen. There was not a patch of white on it and the muscles rippled in its body with every movement. He was spirited too, that much she could see from the impatient little jerk of his head as he pulled at the reins, and the way his hooves pawed at the ground.

'That's Prince,' Conrad told her. 'He's a one-man horse, so don't ever try to ride him.'

Vicky glanced at Conrad quickly and knew by the stern expression on his face that his words had been a warning well worth heeding.

'You're not nervous, are you?' he asked as he helped her into the saddle.

'A little,' she confessed apologetically. 'It's been such a long time.'

'You'll soon get the feel of the horse beneath you and then your nervousness will disappear.'

It was as Conrad had said it would be. Patiently he gave instructions, explaining how her own movements should coincide with those of her mount, and Vicky found it easy to follow his directions.

'You're a born horsewoman,' he said eventually.

Vicky flushed with pleasure at the unexpected compliment and Conrad laughed at her. Drawing his horse up alongside hers, he said: 'In this permissive age women don't blush any more. You're unique.'

Again the colour flooded her cheeks and hastily she looked away, but not before he had noticed.

'You're blushing again,' he told her.

'I am not!'

'Oh, yes, you are!' he insisted and, leaning over in his saddle, he placed his hand in the nape of her neck and pulled her face towards him so that she was forced to look at him. 'Don't ever lose the ability to blush. It suits you, and it's what I like most about you.'

He kissed her then, full on the lips, before moving away from her. 'Come, I want to show you something.'

As if in a trance, she urged on her mount and followed him. How superb he looked, she thought, as she watched him riding ahead of her. How characteristic that Conrad should have chosen a horse that displayed as proud a countenance as he himself.

On a slight rise he stopped and waited for Vicky to come alongside him. 'The original boundary to the farm used to be here,' he told her, pulling down the brim of his hat to shade his eyes from the sun. 'It now lies beyond that small *kopje* in the distance.'

'The farm is bigger than I thought,' she breathed in awe. 'How do you manage to cope on your own?'

'I have no difficulty in coping and my coloured labourers are excellent workers.'

'What happens when you aren't here?' she asked, stealing a glance at him.

'When I'm not here, Jim takes control,' he said. 'Come on, I'll race you to those shady trees.'

And he started out across the veld. 'That's not fair,' Vicky shouted as she chased after him on Teresa. 'You should have warned me that you had something like this in mind.'

Conrad's laughter rang out across the veld, and no matter how much encouragement she lavished on Teresa, they just could not overtake Prince and his rider.

Vicky was breathless by the time she caught up with him. Her hair had come undone from the vigorous ride and she tied it back with a scarf, while Conrad sat watching her with laughter in his eyes.

'I don't know why you tie your hair up the way you do,' he said. 'It looks perfectly lovely when you leave it down.'

'It makes me feel untidy.'

Conrad laughed briefly. 'You no longer have to look like the prim and proper secretary, you know.'

His innocent remark brought her back sharply to the reality of her present situation and sudden tears sprang to her eyes as she gazed out to where the sheep were lazily grazing in the veld.

How different this all was from the plush-carpeted, air-conditioned little office which had become her personal domain over the past years. Life had been so simple, so orderly, so unemotional, and then, unexpectedly, everything seemed to go wrong. It was like walking into a house of mirrors at a fun-fair to see yourself being twisted out of all proportion. From the moment Conrad had walked into her life she had changed from the rational person she was, into an emotional bundle of insecurity and indecision, and Michael had helped to increase the upheaval.

She felt a tug at her hair. 'Missing the city life already?'

'I miss the familiar routine,' she admitted truthfully.

The hand on her hair moved to her shoulder, its pressure increasing slightly before he released her. His touch had been understanding and reassuring and Vicky glanced at him thankfully.

The sun was warm on her arms and back, and deep within her something stirred, yet before she was able to grasp it, it had gone. A fleeting awareness, that left no trace of its identity.

'Where is Michael?' she asked quietly.

'Checking on the jackal fencing. I've lost a number of sheep lately.'

'Is he alone?'

'No, Jim is with him.' He swung his horse round. 'Come, it's time we returned to the homestead. You've done enough riding for one day, and I should warn you that your muscles will most probably be aching tomorrow.'

'I shan't mind at all,' she replied. 'I've enjoyed every minute of the ride.'

Vicky's spirits seemed to slump when she eventually found herself alone at home once more. The ride with Conrad had been wonderful, if somewhat impaired by her own inadequacy. Conrad had been exceedingly patient with her, and all the time she had been aware of him like an electrifying current making her nerves tingle. She shook herself at these disturbing thoughts. It was positively ridiculous that someone, especially Conrad, should have this effect on her, yet she had been even more aware of his magnetism when he placed his hands about her slim waist to lift her off her horse. He had put her gently on her feet in front of him, his hands lingering at her waist.

She halted beside the closed door in the passage. Should she? Conrad had said that she could explore as much as she wished, but ... she dropped her outstretched hand and took a step away. No! The living-room and dining-room doors stood open, but this one remained closed. Perhaps it was his private sanctum. His study? the thought flashed through her mind. Would it matter so much if she merely took a look?

Overcome with curiosity, Vicky tried the handle. It was not locked. She opened the door and went inside, closing it firmly behind her and leaning against it until the wild beating of her heart had subsided.

There was nothing mysterious about this room, after all. It *was* Conrad's study, and something of his personality was revealed to her in what she saw. It was not a big room, and the large ebony desk almost dwarfed it. There was no window except for the double glass doors leading out on to the stoep, and the heavy curtains hanging in front of them were drawn aside to allow ample light to filter through. Besides the leather swivel chair behind the desk, there were two comfortable easy chairs, each with a delicately crocheted cloth draped over the head-rest. Further along the wall stood a brown leather bench, obviously old, judging by its appearance. The entire wall behind the desk was lined with books that looked frighteningly learned, except for a few volumes of poetry which adorned the lowest shelf.

She glanced about her curiously. The room was certainly tidy. Not a thing was out of place, and the desk strangely uncluttered. Either Conrad spent very little time in this room, or he was methodical and meticulously neat.

There were several photographs on the walls and Vicky examined each one with interest. They were mostly photographs of rugby teams, and with each one she had little difficulty in finding Conrad. He was always the tallest one in the back row, with his chin lifted in that arrogant gesture. On his desk were two photographs, one of a girl who was fair and lovely; his sister judging by the inscription at the bottom. 'To dearest Conrad, with love from Barbara.'

The other photograph on the desk was one of himself and his sister. He stood with his arm slung carelessly about her shoulders, and they were both laughing. His hair hung in an unruly fashion across his forehead and somehow softened the lean, hard features, giving him a carefree appearance Vicky had not expected of him. She lifted the photograph and held it in her hands for a moment. Even as a young man he was tall and broad-shouldered, his hips narrow, his thighs muscular. His sister, however, was short, her head barely touching his heart. She was slender and pretty, and decidedly feminine. It was obvious that they were very fond of each other, and Vicky envied her her relaxed appearance as she stood beside her brother. Their relationship with each other was most probably without strain, she thought, and there would certainly be no need for Barbara to feel tense and nervous in her brother's company as she, Vicky felt each time he came near her.

That evening, on her way down to dinner, Vicky once again paused beneath the portrait of the fair young woman in the blue dress that matched the colour of her eyes. She was beautiful, her features delicately modelled as though someone had taken great pains with them, while the eyebrows were slightly raised, giving her a gently teasing, curiously mysterious expression.

Vicky stared once again at the perfect contours of her face, and sighed. All at once she was aware of someone standing behind her and knew instinctively that it was Conrad. Afraid to turn, she remained with her back towards him, clutching her hands nervously in front of her.

'She's beautiful,' she remarked with sincerity. 'Who is she?'

'My great-grandmother, Abigail de Jongh,' he said. He moved to Vicky's side and leaned against the wall so that he could look down at her. He had discarded his working clothes and was dressed in dark trousers that flared only slightly at the bottom. Her glance travelled upwards to the muscular thighs, the slim hips and the silky white shirt

72

which was open at the neck to reveal the tanned column of his throat and a smattering of dark hair on his chest. His grey eyes regarded her lazily and her pulse quickened as she realised that she had been staring.

'Perhaps this is the appropriate time to tell you something about Great-grandmother Abigail,' he observed, folding his arms across his broad chest. 'It will also explain how Duiwelspoort acquired its name.'

'Was Duiwelspoort originally known by another name?' Vicky asked, her interest quickening.

Conrad nodded. 'Duiwelspoort was originally called "Honeydew" and it belonged to a family by the name of Baxter. Old man Baxter had no sons, only one daughter, Abigail. Baxter was a sickly man and the farm eventually became too much for him to handle on his own. He split it in two, selling the other half to my great-grandfather, Lourens de Jongh, and at the same time acquiring a farm-hand to help him on his remaining portion. The hired man, according to Abigail, was a great hulking brute of a man, with shifty eyes. He took one look at Abigail and that's when the trouble started. Stevens, that was his name, wanted Abigail, and Abigail loved my great-grandfather Lourens. By all accounts, Stevens was quite insanely in love with Abigail and is reputed to have threatened to kill her rather than see her married to anyone else.'

Vicky, absorbed in the story, sucked her breath in sharply. 'Did he actually try to kill her?'

'Yes, he tried, but we're jumping ahead a bit. None of the family took his threat seriously, least of all Abigail. Lourens did, though, and made a point of following her about without her knowledge just in case Stevens decided to carry out his threat. As it happened it was as well that he had dogged her footsteps, for she was strolling through the orchard late one afternoon when Stevens accosted her. The more she fought him off, the more he became inflamed by his passion for her until, in desperation, he tried to strangle her.'

'No!' Vicky's stomach twisted into a knot at the thought of that lovely neck in the hands of a madman.

'Fortunately Lourens was close at hand and he managed to drag the man off her. Great-grandfather Lourens was a big man and Stevens only slightly smaller, but Stevens had the added strength of a madman. Stevens went berserk at the interruption, but Lourens, nevertheless, managed to knock him senseless. With the help of Abigail, Lourens tied Stevens' hands and feet before taking him to the local police station. He was eventually declared insane and he committed suicide several months later. My coloured labourers swear that he still roams the orchards at night in search of Abigail.'

'And does he?'

Conrad laughed. 'I can't say that I've ever seen anything, and I often take a short cut through the orchard at night.'

Vicky dropped her gaze before his. 'You still haven't explained how Duiwelspoort acquired its name.'

Conrad pushed himself away from the wall and stood behind Vicky once more. 'Abigail often teased my great-grandfather playfully by calling him "*duiwel*". I am told that whenever she recounted the events of that afternoon she would remark on the fact that my great-grandfather had to fight like the very devil to save her honour, and her life. When old Mr Baxter died, Abigail inherited his farm and the two farms became a whole once more.' Conrad's hands came down heavily on to her shoulders. 'It's Abigail who renamed it Duiwelspoort.'

Vicky stared up at Abigail's portrait and found it almost impossible to believe that someone so calm and serene could have lived through such a terrible ordeal. She must have been terribly frightened, the now calm, smiling eyes wide with horror. There was a hint of amusement in those eyes now as they smiled down at Vicky, or was it merely imagination, she wondered. Abigail was certainly beautiful, Vicky admitted to herself once again, and it was little wonder that Stevens, unfortunate man, should have fallen so madly in love with her.

Conrad's grip tightened on her shoulders as he turned her to face him. 'Does it comfort you to know that the de Jongh men are not devils as the name of the farm suggests?'

'I'm not sure whether I should feel comforted or not,' Vicky replied with a certain amount of humour. 'Those were the days when chivalrous deeds were the order of the day. Would you, if you had to, be chivalrous enough to fight a madman to save the honour of the woman you loved?'

Conrad released her suddenly, his face an expressionless mask. 'That depends entirely on whether she's worth fighting for.'

During the ensuing silence, Vicky was surprised at herself for having had the temerity to ask such a question. What business was it of hers, after all, what Conrad would do in a situation like that, and why should his reply have had the power to hurt her?

'That is a portrait of my great-grandfather, Lourens de Jongh,' Conrad pointed out.

Vicky glanced at it in surprise. She had been so enchanted by the portrait of Abigail that she had not noticed the portrait hanging alongside it, and a slight shock ran through her. But for the moustache, it could have been Conrad she was looking at. The only difference was in the eyes. Where Conrad's eyes were always either cold, guarded or teasing, Lourens de Jongh's eyes revealed what she was sure he had intended them to. Had his thoughts perhaps been with his beloved Abigail when that portrait had been painted? She wondered curiously. She tried to imagine Conrad looking at her with that same look in his eyes, and quite suddenly a warning signal screamed along her nerves and made her tremble.

'There is a definite likeness between yourself and your great-grandfather,' Vicky remarked, keeping her voice casual as they went down the stairs.

'Do you think so?'

'Yes. Excepting for the moustache, of course.'

'Would you like me to grow one?'

Vicky replied a little too sharply, 'Suit yourself.'

Conrad appeared to stiffen beside her, his expression becoming austere, and definitely mocking. 'Some women don't like me with a moustache. They say it tickles when they're kissed.'

Vicky's cheeks were stained a delicate pink. 'I—I wouldn't know.'

'Perhaps I should grow one, then, so that you can tell me if this is so,' Conrad persisted relentlessly.

Lizzie appeared, announcing that dinner was ready, and Vicky was mercifully saved from having to reply.

Michael, sunburnt and obviously suffering from physical fatigue, was silently morose throughout dinner. On several occasions she tried to draw him into the conversation, without much success, until she noticed Conrad's tight-lipped expression. It was then that she realised with clarity that Conrad would drive Michael relentlessly until he was literally ready to drop. He would make it his business to get his money's worth out of Michael, regardless of Michael's physical inferiority compared to his own stature and strength. The thought horrified her and she suddenly felt a great pity for Michael. He was so young, and so used to getting his own way. He had been spoilt from childhood and after their mother's death Vicky had merely picked up where she had left off. She had given him his way in everything, and had made herself available whenever he had needed her. As the older sister, she had always been there to pull him out of the scrapes he had got himself into, and she had managed perfectly well until this last occasion. Now Michael would have to pay for his deed as she was paying for her own folly throughout the years, and Conrad, despite the charm that quite often filtered through, would be a hard task-master.

Michael excused himself immediately after dinner and went to his room. Alone with Conrad, Vicky thought it an opportune moment to speak to him about her brother.

'Conrad, don't be too harsh on him,' she pleaded nervously.

Conrad's glance became razor-sharp. 'He would have received no leniency in prison. Here he is at least free.'

'He would eventually have repaid the money he—borrowed.'

'Say it!' Conrad snapped. 'The money he stole!' He threw his table-napkin on to the table and stood up, his chair scraping violently on the wooden floor. 'You might as well face facts, Vicky. The case against him was for fraud. Do you know what that means?'

Her lips parted, but no sound came as she stared up at him white-faced.

'He not only cooked the firm's books, in plain language, but he also copied the manager's signature on to vouchers for the amount he took.' Conrad's chest heaved slightly, but he showed no pity as he drove the facts home. 'It was a clear-cut case of fraud!'

Vicky felt her insides shiver as the truth was made known to her. 'It's partially my fault!' she cried clenching her hands so tightly in her lap that her nails bit into the palms. 'I'm as much to blame as he is.'

There was a brief silence, and then, 'I dare say you are,' his cruel words lashed her. 'You pampered him too much, you never questioned him when he continually borrowed money from you to pay his debts, and you went on to the bitter end doing just that until you had to degrade yourself by borrowing money from a stranger to get him out of trouble.'

'He's my brother!' she bit out angrily. 'And you didn't have to lend me the money. You could have refused.'

Conrad's eyes narrowed as he stared down at her, his hands doubled into fists at his side. 'Yes, I could have refused,' he said slowly, advancing towards her. A tremor of fear shook her as he reached out a hand, but he merely grasped her chin and lifted her face in order to look long and hard into her eyes. 'I could have refused,' he repeated, 'but I didn't. I married you instead, and saved my wife and myself the embarrassment of her brother going to prison.'

'I dare say we shall have to pay dearly for your kindness,' she remarked sarcastically, her eyes smarting.

'Yes,' he replied, his lips twisting cruelly. 'You shall pay.'

'And may I ask what form of payment you will demand from me?'

Her throat tightened with fear as she stared up into his hard face, and a warning voice told her that she was goading him too far.

'There is only one way a woman can pay,' he mocked cynically.

'I'd rather die!' she cried, wrenching herself free from his grasp and making a dash for the door, but Conrad was there first, his hands like bands of steel about her wrists and making her cry out with pain.

'You need not fear that ... yet,' he hissed through his teeth, and she was only too aware of the power he wielded over her. 'I shall extract payment from you when I feel the time is right for it.'

'You said our marriage would be a business arrangement,' she accused.

'Did I?'

'You know you did,' she bit out the words frantically. 'Are you so dishonourable that you would break your word?'

He freed her suddenly. 'Whether I break my word depends entirely on you, my dear. We shall have to wait and see.'

Vicky did not wait to hear more but wrenched open the door and fled up the stairs to her room where she stood for endless seconds staring at the communicating door, realising her helplessness if he should ever feel the need to walk through it to claim the payment he had spoken of.

CHAPTER FIVE

The atmosphere at Duiwelspoort remained peculiarly tense and Michael's behaviour did nothing to ease the situation. An antagonism had sprung up between himself and Conrad that had become almost tangible, and it usually reached its peak during the evening meal they shared together. Michael's blistered hands caused Vicky minor concern, but it was the look of utter exhaustion on his face each evening that really angered her. It would be useless, she realised, to confront Conrad with her protests unless she was prepared to endure another scene like the previous one.

To counteract the loneliness, Vicky often spent time in the kitchen with Lizzie and, to her amazement, she actually began to learn the intricacies of the coal stove under Lizzie's careful guidance. It was during one such session, a few mornings later, that Michael came bursting into the kitchen while Vicky and Lizzie were baking biscuits. Vicky had just removed the hot pan from the oven when the door flew open and Michael stormed in.

'You'd better prepare yourself,' he announced angrily. 'That Natalie woman was here again to invite us to have dinner with them this evening, and Conrad accepted.'

'Michael?' Vicky began, perplexed, but he had already left the kitchen and was bounding up the stairs to his room.

A frown of irritation creased her brow, but the next instant the hot pan was burning her through the oven glove and she dropped it with a clatter on the table.

'Oh, dear,' she muttered, surveying the scattered biscuits and making an effort to retrieve them.

'Don't worry, Madam, I'll do that,' Lizzie offered kindly

while Vicky stood there wondering what would be the outcome of the latest storm-clouds gathering about her.

'Master Michael doesn't like it much here on the farm,' Lizzie observed sadly.

'No.' What would be the use of denying it?

'Why did he come here, then, Madam?'

Vicky noticed the sincere concern in Lizzie's dark eyes and wished that she could have told her the truth.

'He—wanted to get away from the city for a while,' she replied hesitantly. That in itself was not altogether an untruth. 'Farming is a far more strenuous occupation than the one he had in the city,' Vicky tried, making excuses for him. 'Perhaps it is merely tiredness that is affecting him in this way.'

Lizzie did not reply to that and obviously had her own thoughts on the matter. She, too, must have sensed the atmosphere prevailing in the house and Vicky wondered how she had interpreted it.

Luncheon was a silent affair until Conrad spoke. 'Natalie was here this morning,' he began casually. 'We have been——'

'I have already told Vicky about it,' Michael interrupted in a surly voice.

Conrad's knife and fork clattered on to his plate, and Vicky jumped nervously. 'I was not aware of the fact that I had asked you to act as spokesman for me?'

'What difference does it make who told her?'

'I am quite capable of speaking for myself, thank you.'

The ice in Conrad's voice chilled Vicky to the marrow. 'Oh, please, please,' she pleaded. 'It really doesn't matter who told me. Please don't argue about it.'

Conrad's glance was withering and Vicky shrank from it. 'Don't interfere. This matter concerns Michael and myself,' he ordered sharply.

'I shan't be going,' Michael announced stubbornly.

'You will go even if I have to drag you every inch of the way,' Conrad announced forcefully, and the look of determination on his face indicated that he would do just that, if necessary.

As on so many other occasions over the past few days, Michael pushed his plate aside and left the dining-room, leaving Conrad and Vicky to finish their meal in silence. Vicky pushed her fork through her food for a while and then she, too, pushed her plate aside, but as she was about to leave the table she found her wrist caught in a grip that sent a sharp pain shooting up her arm. She winced and subsided into her chair.

'You will remain seated until I have finished eating,' Conrad said in a voice that was deathly calm, and Vicky obeyed him without a murmur.

'You may pour me a cup of coffee,' he instructed eventually, 'and pour yourself a cup as well.'

'I don't want any.'

'Do as you're told,' he said coldly.

'I refuse to be ordered about like a child,' she exclaimed with a spurt of anger which she instantly regretted at the sight of the fury on his face.

'Don't try me too far, Vicky,' he said ominously, the muscles in his cheeks bunched into knots.

Without a word Vicky poured them each a cup of coffee, her hand trembling visibly as she placed his before him, splashing some of the liquid into the saucer.

The drank their coffee in absolute silence, although Vicky felt that she would choke with every mouthful she took. At that moment she wished desperately for the calm, peaceful life she had led before she had met Conrad, and before ...! Poor Michael ... she could not blame him entirely for landing her in this situation. She had not been forced to accept Conrad's help. She could have ... what? Gone to the Bank? Sam? Her boss? Allowed Michael to go to prison? No! No! No! She would far rather suffer the consequences of her rash decision than have had that happen!

'Does Michael necessarily have to come with us to the van Buurens' this evening?' Vicky asked tentatively.

'We are sociable people here in the Karroo and it's the neighbourly thing to do to invite your friends over occasionally,' Conrad informed her stiffly. 'Sonia van Buuren would feel insulted if Michael didn't come with us, considering that she specifically invited him as well.'

'Couldn't we——'

'Vicky!' he warned. 'I will not have people speculating about the non-appearance of your brother.'

'But——'

'The subject is closed!'

It was three very silent people who drove to the neighbouring farm that evening. When Vicky had come down into the hall before their departure she had been surprised to find Conrad and Michael waiting there for her. She had no way of knowing whether there had been a necessity for another altercation between them, but Michael had appeared quite docile, and had even managed to give her a welcoming smile.

Vicky had chosen a full-length cherry-coloured evening dress with long sleeves, the scalloped neckline showing off her slender neck to perfection. Her only adornment was a string of cultured pearls which had originally belonged to her mother.

Conrad's glance had swept over her with apparent approval, taking in the slender waist below which the skirt flared slightly.

'You look lovely, darling,' he had remarked as she reached his side, but this was naturally for Michael's benefit, she had told herself.

Otto and Sonia van Buuren were not at all what Vicky had expected. They were charming, warm-hearted people who immediately welcomed Michael and herself into their home as though they were old friends. Natalie, of course, swooped down on Conrad, and made it her business to see that he remained almost constantly at her side.

The only other member of the family Vicky had not known of was the van Buurens' son, Rodney. He was obviously several years older than Natalie, but not much older than Vicky herself. There was a remarkable likeness between him and his sister, except that his face was a little too rugged to be called beautiful, but he was definitely handsome, with a charming manner to boost that quality.

Vicky was a little worried about Michael at first, but he and Otto van Buuren obviously took a liking to each other and Vicky noticed them chatting together for quite some time.

Sonia's dinner, when it was served, was quite superb, yet nothing elaborate. There was the tenderest mutton Vicky had ever tasted, with mint sauce, and potatoes roasted to a crisp with fresh garden peas and diced carrots. Not since her first evening meal at Duiwelspoort had Vicky enjoyed her food so much, and with Rodney beside her she felt relaxed, often laughing at his quaint remarks.

On several occasions she looked up to find Conrad's eyes upon her, his gaze disturbing, but Rodney inevitably claimed her attention and she thought no more about it.

'I must say we were tremendously surprised to hear that you were married, Conrad,' Sonia remarked during dinner. 'How on earth did you manage to remain so secretive about your intentions?'

'Actually, I had no intention of getting married yet,' Conrad told them matter-of-factly. 'Vicky talked me into it.'

To her mortification Vicky felt her cheeks go hot amid

the laughter, and the glance she shot at him was almost venomous.

'Did I say something wrong, darling?' Conrad asked, smiling placidly.

Vicky could cheerfully have throttled him. 'No, darling,' she replied, her voice equally sweet. 'When a man has managed to remain a bachelor for as long as you did, he quite naturally doesn't like the idea of people knowing that he, like the others, has finally succumbed to a woman's charms.'

Amid the laughter following her remark, their glances met and held; his inscrutable, hers portraying wide-eyed innocence. An unfathomable expression crossed his face as he inclined his head in her direction.

'I can see you'll have to be careful in future, Conrad,' Otto remarked laughingly. 'Your wife isn't as timid as her appearance suggests.'

'You're right, Otto. There are many facets to my wife's character I have yet to discover.' Conrad smiled lazily in her direction. 'The prospect is utterly pleasing, and very tantalising.'

Natalie was not too pleased with the way things were going and she changed the subject swiftly.

'You must come over tomorrow some time and have a look at our new foal,' she said quickly, placing her slender hand on his arm.

Conrad glanced down at Natalie and smiled. 'I'll come over as soon as I have a moment to spare,' he promised.

When they finally returned to the living-room, Vicky found herself seated beside Rodney once more.

'Your wedding *was* rather sudden,' he remarked, returning to the remark his mother had passed at the dinner table. 'I'm afraid the news knocked the ground from beneath our feet, so to speak.'

'I'm sorry,' Vicky lowered her glance, 'but it wasn't really all that sudden.'

'You've known each other for quite some time, then?'

'Not——' She hesitated suddenly, biting her lip. 'Not very long. We met a couple of times when—whenever he was in Cape Town.'

'You mean it was love at first sight?'

Vicky felt as though she was floundering in dangerous waters. 'Well ... I—I suppose you could say that.'

'Hm ... marry in haste, repent at leisure,' he murmured softly.

She glanced at him swiftly. 'Are you suggesting that it will be that way with Conrad and myself?'

'No!' He looked startled. 'I was merely thinking of the old adage about marrying in haste and all that sort of thing. I must say old Conrad certainly knows how to pick a winner.'

'I—I beg your pardon?' It was Vicky's turn to look startled.

Rodney smiled. 'You're very attractive, you know.'

'I'm glad you didn't say beautiful, because that would have been a downright lie,' she reacted flippantly.

'Beauty is quite often only skin deep,' Rodney told her, his eyes appraising her quite openly. 'A woman who is attractive usually has character.'

Natalie's laughter at the other end of the room claimed her attention. 'Your sister is beautiful.'

'Yes,' he laughed, 'and she knows it. But she's only eighteen, and on the threshold of womanhood when a girl still places much importance on her outward beauty, which generally only attracts the wrong kind of man.'

'I suppose so.'

'At the moment she's in no danger, for she's concentrating her attention on Conrad.' There was the slightest pause. 'Why do you allow her to flirt so openly with him?'

'If it amuses her to flirt with my—husband,' Vicky hesitated a moment. It was the first time she had actually spoken of Conrad in that capacity, and the most peculiar emotion took possession of her. 'If it amuses her,' she rushed on, 'then I have no objection.'

'You're not jealous?' Rodney glanced at her in disbelief.

'No.'

Liar! a small voice accused. Why does the ease in their manner towards each other disturb you so much? Why does each smile he bestows on her make you wish you were the recipient? They were uncomfortable thoughts that were best left unanswered if she wished to emerge from this marriage unscathed, she decided firmly.

The drive back to Duiwelspoort later that evening was quite pleasant, for Conrad's mood seemed lighter than when they had gone.

'It appears as though you enjoyed the evening, Michael,' he remarked pleasantly over his shoulder. 'Not sorry you went?'

'No,' Michael admitted. 'They're genuinely nice people.'

'Yes, they are,' Conrad agreed, concentrating on the road.

Conrad dropped them off at the front door and drove off to the garage.

'Vicky,' Michael began uncertainly as they slowly mounted the steps on to the stoep. 'Why did you marry Conrad?'

'What a strange question!' she laughed shakily.

'But I'm asking it,' he insisted urgently, his face sharply etched against the starlit sky. 'Why?'

'Because—because I—love him,' the words came with difficulty. She would have to be careful not to let Michael realise the truth, she realised nervously, and her reply had been far too hesitant to sound convincing.

'Are you sure?'

'Yes, yes,' she replied more firmly. 'I love him.'

'Why did you allow Natalie to flirt with him so outrageously this evening?'

It was the second time someone was asking her that question in one evening and Vicky was finding it more difficult to reply to.

'Was she flirting with him?' she asked vaguely, trying to avoid the issue.

'You know jolly well she was,' Michael retorted angrily, thrusting his hands into his pockets and hunching his shoulders. 'Didn't you mind?'

'Of course I did,' she replied evenly, hoping that her voice sounded reassuring enough. 'But I couldn't very well have made a fuss about it, could I? It would have been embarrassing, not only to myself, but to our hosts.'

A thoughtful silence followed this remark. 'I suppose you're right,' Michael admitted grudgingly, and apparently satisfied.

Vicky sighed with relief as Conrad appeared and they entered the house. Michael excused himself instantly and rushed upstairs while Conrad and Vicky followed more slowly. Neither of them spoke until they reached her door, then Conrad pushed it open and, to her dismay, followed her in, closing the door firmly behind him.

For a moment she stared at him, her nerves taut. Then, determined not to let him see that his presence had unnerved her, she turned her back on him and walked as naturally as she could across to the dressing-table, placing her wrap and evening bag on the stool before it.

'You can relax,' he said suddenly behind her, making her jump. 'For some reason Michael was standing just outside his bedroom door watching us. Didn't you see him?'

'No, I didn't.' She swung round to face him, relieved that her fears had been unfounded.

'Do you think he suspects something?' Conrad asked.

Vicky recalled the conversation she had had with Michael

while they had been waiting on the stoep for Conrad to join them. 'I don't think he's altogether convinced that I—that we——' She faltered, unable to continue. Conrad stood with eyebrows raised, waiting for her to continue, and obviously not intending to help her out. 'He's beginning to doubt my reasons for marrying you,' she ended in a rush, lowering her glance to his dark necktie.

'What makes you so sure of that?'

'He—he——' she swallowed at the constriction in her throat. 'He questioned me while we were waiting for you to garage the Holden.'

'What sort of questions?' Conrad went on relentlessly.

Vicky made a helpless little gesture with her hands. 'He wanted to know why I'd married you.'

'And?' His eyes glittered.

'I told him that I'd married you because— because I c-cared for you.' The colour suffused her cheeks and she turned away, fiddling with her hairbrush on the dresser.

'Is that the word you used? Cared?'

'I—I—oh, for heaven's sake, Conrad!' she swung round angrily. 'Isn't it enough to know that I tried to reassure him? Must you know in detail every word I uttered?'

'I just thought that if I was Michael I wouldn't feel very reassured if you used the word "cared". A woman doesn't marry a man simply because she "cares" for him.'

'I didn't use the word "cared".' She lowered her glance once more, veiling her eyes. 'I said that I l-loved you.'

There was absolute silence for a moment and Vicky glanced up to discover a mocking look on his face. She stared at him incredulously, her anger mounting steadily.

'You beast!' she cried, her eyes dark with anger. 'You did this on purpose.'

'I had to get my own back because of a certain remark you passed at the dinner table.'

'I only said what I did because of the remark you passed

in the first place,' Vicky reminded him, her anger simmering. 'Do you mean to tell me that Michael wasn't in the passage watching us?'

'No, that was the truth,' he replied. 'He was in the passage, and he was watching us.'

Vicky's glance was sceptical.

'It's the truth, so help me,' he said, raising his right hand with mock solemnity. His gaze travelled over her and finally came to rest on her hair. 'It's your own fault if people become suspicious. I told you once before you don't look like a woman who's been kissed, and kissed often.'

Vicky's cheeks felt hot. 'Oh, go away! I wish you would leave me in peace!'

She turned away, placing her hands against her cheeks and wishing desperately that she could learn to control the pulse that throbbed so wildly at the base of her throat. Oh, why did Conrad not go and leave her alone! She felt his hands in her hair the next moment and flung up her hands protectively.

'No! No, don't!' But it was too late. Her hair came tumbling down to her shoulders and Conrad was running his fingers through it as though it fascinated him.

Vicky stood perfectly still, staring at him in the mirror and wondering why the sight of him standing there, with her hair in his hands, should have this effect on her. He looked up then and their eyes met in the mirror, his expression sending a tremor through her body.

'You have beautiful hair, Vicky,' he said thickly, twisting it gently around his hand. 'It's the colour of ripe corn, and as soft as silk. Why don't you leave it like this? Why do you always twist it up into a knot in the nape of your neck?'

'It's the only way I can keep it in order.'

'Don't ever cut your hair,' he said then, and as his fingers touched her neck she began to tremble.

'I'm quite often tempted to do just that.'

'Don't!' he said sharply, and with such intensity that it frightened her. 'Don't ever cut your hair.'

Sheer nervousness made her laugh then. 'Really, Conrad, you sound almost dictatorial!'

He laughed slightly and helped her retrieve the hairpins he had scattered on the floor.

'You obviously enjoyed yourself this evening,' he remarked, dropping a handful of pins into her outstretched palm and straightening.

'Yes, as a matter of fact, I did.'

'Rodney was definitely smitten. He hardly left your side.'

'I could say exactly the same about Natalie and you.' The atmosphere was tense.

'Were you jealous?' he asked mockingly.

'Were you?'

The moment those words were uttered Vicky could have kicked herself, and she had even more reason to despise herself when she suddenly found herself trapped against the broadness of his chest, the rough material of his jacket beneath her fingertips as she tried to push him away.

'Don't be too clever, Vicky, you're likely to get hurt,' he said darkly, lowering his head.

Vicky twisted her head from side to side to avoid his lips until she felt a sharp tug at her hair, jerking her face upwards.

'Please, Conrad, don't!' she cried, but he merely laughed, lowering his head and caressing her lips with his own until she begged once more against his lips that he should stop.

The room revolved around her and she struggled against him as the pressure of his lips increased, but his arms merely tightened about her, making her efforts futile. His kiss lingered on until every nerve in her body seemed to tingle in response. She relaxed then, savouring the sweet enchantment of the moment as Conrad's hands moved down the hollow of her back, pressing her closer still to him.

Sanity returned as she realised, with a shock of horror, exactly what she was doing. She was allowing Conrad to make love to her, and she was actually ... enjoying it! What on earth had made her respond in this way? What must he think of her?

Fierce shame gave her added strength and she struggled free from his arms, her breath coming fast over lips still warm and tingling from his kisses.

'You had no right to do that!' she accused, her voice rasping in her throat.

Conrad reached out for her, the light of passion in his eyes filling her with alarm.

'Don't touch me!' she snapped, jerking away from him. Ragged nerves and burning shame made her careless of her choice of words. 'I'd rather die than have you touch me again. I can't bear it, and I hate you!'

Conrad went white, his eyes like two blades of steel raked her from head to foot. 'What makes you think I should ever want to touch you again? Don't overestimate your charms, my dear. You don't possess the type of beauty that would ever have the power to drive a man to the brink of passion.'

His words lashed her cruelly, sending every vestige of colour from her face as he strode past her, closing the communicating door behind him with a decisive click.

Vicky's legs gave way beneath her as violent tremors shook her slender frame. She fell across the bed, clutching at the silken bedspread as if for support. Her eyes were stinging with unshed tears, and in her heart there raged a storm of remorse accompanied with a pain so terrible that it seemed to tear her apart.

The days passed with agonising slowness on Duiwelspoort,

dragging through June and into July. In Michael's presence they continued the pretence of being happily married, with Conrad lavishing endearments on Vicky which echoed mockingly through her tortured mind as she lay awake each night, staring into the darkness.

Winter had set in with a vengeance and although Vicky had not intended using the allowance Conrad had made her, she was eventually forced to admit defeat and drove in to town one morning to buy herself warmer clothes. Her winter wardrobe would have sufficed in Cape Town, but it was far from adequate against the sting of the Karroo winters.

Koelenberg did not have a large variety of clothing to offer but, despite this, Vicky managed to buy herself a few warm woollen slacks and sweaters, one or two frocks for the day and an evening dress of the palest blue that flared out entrancingly from her slender waist. The sleeves were wide with a broad cuff, and the high neckline had a touch of lace that gave her a slightly old-fashioned appearance as well as accentuating the proud tilt to her head and the straight, slim shoulders.

It surprised her to discover that everyone in town apparently knew who she was, and she was treated with such cordiality wherever she went that she no longer felt a stranger to the district, almost as though she had lived there all her life. There was no need to search for anything, for everyone seemed only too eager to direct her. Halfway through her shopping spree, Vicky enjoyed a cup of tea in a delightfully quaint tea room, and it was there that Rodney van Buuren found her.

'Hello,' he said, joining her at her table. 'We haven't seen you for a long time. Still living high in the realms of wedded bliss?'

Vicky merely smiled, hoping that it would be convincing enough. 'Are you joining me for tea?'

'If you have no objection.'

The waitress came and took his order and while he waited he lit a cigarette, glancing at her speculatively through a haze of smoke.

'You look tired,' he remarked with concern, pointing to the faint shadows beneath her eyes. 'Has Conrad been manhandling you?'

'Don't be silly!'

'You're not ill?' he persisted.

'I'm perfectly well.'

Vicky lowered her glance and refilled her cup. How could she explain her dreadfully unhappy state? Would he understand ... would anyone understand, that being unable to discover the reason for her unhappiness, it only made her feel immeasurably worse?

Rodney's tea arrived and Vicky poured for him. 'Are you in town on business?' she asked conversationally, handing him his cup.

'I came in to get a spare part for our truck.' He took a mouthful of tea and smiled. 'And you? Are you alone, or are you expecting Conrad?'

'I came in alone.'

'With the Holden?' He looked somewhat surprised.

'Yes. Why?'

'I'm just surprised, that's all. Conrad has never let anyone but himself touch that Holden.' There was a slight pause. 'I can only think that he must love you quite to distraction to allow you to drive it.'

'I can only think that he must love you quite to distraction', Rodney's words raced through her mind as she drove back to Duiwelspoort. 'Love you to distraction. Love you to distraction.' It was ridiculous! If only Rodney knew!

Everything seemed ominously quiet when Vicky reached the homestead. Lizzie, too, seemed less talkative, shaking her head and muttering to herself. A cold hand of fear clutched at Vicky's heart.

'Lizzie, what's wrong? What has happened?'

Lizzie shook her head sadly. 'The Madam mustn't worry. Master Conrad's bark is always worse than his bite.'

'His bark is——?' Vicky stopped, puzzled. What on earth was Lizzie talking about? she wondered. Had something happened while she was away? Michael?

'Michael!' she said sharply, gripping Lizzie's arm. 'Has something happened to Michael? Is that it?'

'*Ag, nee,* Madam, there is nothing wrong with Master Michael,' Lizzie reassured her. 'He is with Master Conrad and Jim, helping them inject some of the sheep.'

'Well, what is it, then?' Vicky demanded impatiently. 'What is wrong?'

'Madam?' Lizzie shook her head. 'I think Madam better wait until Master Conrad is home.'

It would be useless trying to persuade her further, Vicky realised, for Lizzie could be as stubborn as a mule where Conrad was concerned. The only thing to do would be to wait until Conrad was home, and she did not have long to wait either. His heavy footsteps echoed through the hall and even as he walked, he called to her.

'I'm here, Conrad,' she answered, emerging from the kitchen with some trepidation.

He opened the door to his study and even in the shadowy passageway it was not difficult to see that his face was dark with anger.

'Go in,' he said briefly, and with a heavy, thudding heart Vicky did as he had ordered. He closed the door behind him, walked across to his desk and flung his hat on to his chair. He gestured angrily. 'Sit down.'

Vicky lowered herself into the chair and stared a long way up at him where he stood leaning against the desk.

'What's wrong, Conrad?' she whispered fearfully. 'What have I done?'

Conrad snorted, walking away from the desk and pacing about angrily. 'What have you done, you ask? So you realise that you have done something wrong, do you?'

'Conrad, I don't understand——' she faltered, gripping the arms of her chair.

Conrad stopped in front of her, his eyes narrowed and angry, his fists clenched at his sides. 'You went to town this morning,' he said, his nostrils flaring.

'Yes,' she whispered in agreement, a frightened pulse throbbing in her throat.

'Did you close the gates behind you?'

'I——'

'Don't bother lying to me,' he thundered at her, and she stared at him with growing alarm as the realisation dawned upon her. 'You left every single gate open behind you, and one of my best stud rams wandered out through the gate you so conveniently left open, and into the road. There were ewes in the veld across the road and he headed in that direction. A lorry came along at just that moment and——' he drew a shuddering breath, 'I happen to be minus a stud ram which was imported from Australia and which cost me a fortune.'

'Oh, no!' Vicky covered her face with trembling hands. 'Oh, Conrad, I didn't realise——'

'No, you didn't realise!' he shouted at her. 'One of my most explicit instructions has always been, don't leave any gates open. I suppose you thought I was trying to be difficult; trying to be dictatorial; or trying to impress you with my authoritative attitude?'

Vicky trembled violently. 'Conrad, please——'

'Your thoughtlessness has cost me a great deal of money,' he stormed on as though she had not spoken. 'I've spent far more than the purchase price on that ram, and I haven't even had the opportunity to use him!'

Tears smarted her eyes and, filled with remorse, she could only sit there staring at him, wishing there was some way she could compensate him for the loss she had so inadvertently caused.

Conrad's large frame quivered with rage as he bent over her. 'I swore I would never so much as lay a finger on you again,' he hissed at her, 'but, by heavens, I feel like thrashing you!'

Vicky lowered her glance before the intensity of his violent gaze, and wrung her hands together nervously. 'I wouldn't blame you if you did,' she whispered contritely, her head bent.

A heavy silence followed her remark and, afraid to witness his wrath, Vicky kept her eyes riveted to her hands as she waited for ... what? Punishment? A thrashing? She trembled visibly.

'Vicky.'

Her name was uttered hoarsely and her head shot up as though someone had jerked her by the hair. There was no anger on his face now, except a tired, defenceless look, and something else she could not define, but which nevertheless had the power to render her limbs useless while her heart hammered wildly against her ribs.

He sighed heavily and stepped away from her. 'You may go, Vicky,' he said abruptly, 'and if you ever leave gates open again in future ...'

He left his sentence unfinished, but Vicky needed no further words to know exactly what would happen to her. She fled from his study as quickly as her trembling legs would take her and sought out the sanctuary of her room where she could review her actions without Conrad's disturbing presence to clutter up her thoughts.

CHAPTER SIX

VICKY was sitting in the garden one morning, reading through a book of poetry she had found in Conrad's study, when she heard the Holden come up the drive. Conrad must have noticed her instantly for, moments later, he came striding across to where she was sitting on a wooden bench beneath the oak tree.

Vicky watched him surreptitiously and could not help but admire his obvious strength and vitality. Despite his size he was tremendously agile, although his movements were almost deceptively slow. There was not an ounce of superfluous fat on his body, she had noticed once when, stripped to the waist, he had assisted with the loading of bags of fodder on to a trailer. The muscles in his arms and chest had rippled in the sunlight as he lifted each bag with near effortless ease on to the trailer.

Conrad stood before her then, his pipe clenched between his strong white teeth, and a wad of mail in his hands. Since that regrettable occasion when she had left the gates open, Conrad had not offered her the Holden for a trip into town, neither had he suggested taking her with him.

'Here's a letter for you,' he said, dropping a lilac envelope into her lap, and then, to her astonishment, he sat down beside her and proceeded to open his own post.

Acutely conscious of his presence so close beside her, Vicky glanced down at the letter. Her heart leapt with joy as she recognised Hilary's handwriting and she hastily inserted her thumb beneath the flap, ripping it open.

'Dearest Vicky,' Hilary had written. 'It was wonderful to hear from you at last. Sam and I were just beginning to wonder whether you'd forgotten us, and were threatening to do all manner of things if we didn't hear from you within the next few weeks.

'I am enclosing a cheque for eight hundred Rand. Sam sold all your furniture for you, except the hi-fi set. I think he is contemplating buying it himself for the holiday cottage we have bought. This amount also includes a month's rental which they have refunded you now that your flat is once again occupied. It seems funny, somehow, driving past there and knowing that you have left.

'Vicky, are you happy? Your letter was long, but uninformative, and—forgive me, my dear—I can't help but get the feeling that your marriage is not all that it should be. Sam gets angry with me when I say this, but I've remained unconvinced about the reason for your sudden marriage. You were never prone to impulsiveness, Vicky, not as I am, and why, when you've always looked forward to a church wedding with all the trimmings, would you have rushed through that impersonal little ceremony in the register office?

'There is one other thing you ought to know. There's a rumour amongst our mutual friends that Michael was sacked from his job, and they're hinting at fraud. Vicky, I would hate to pry, but as I'm your long and trusted friend, please tell me—is this so? I pray to heaven that this was not the reason for your hasty decision.

'Conrad is a dear, I know, and Sam thinks the world of him. I can't think of anyone I would rather see you married to than him, but not as a form of escape, Vicky. A marriage cannot be built on anything other than mutual love and respect, and I can only pray that, despite my doubts to the contrary, this was the true foundation of your marriage.

'I'm afraid I've been rather outspoken—another failing of mine—and I hope that you will understand and forgive me as you have always done in the past. One of the reasons,

I think, why our friendship has been so strong was the fact that we were at all times truthful with each other. Please write to me, Vicky, and reassure me if you can—I am so desperately anxious about you.

'Please pass on our regards to Conrad. Best love, Hilary.'

Further down the page there was a postscript that puzzled Vicky. It read: 'Sam wants to know what Conrad thought of the wedding present he had given him. It all sounds frightfully mysterious. Do you know anything about it?'

Vicky slowly lowered the letter. So Hilary had not been fooled by the little charade they had enacted, and knowing Vicky so well she had sensed that something was amiss. Vicky sighed and stared into the distance, vaguely aware that Conrad had long since discarded his post and that he sat watching her thoughtfully.

'Is it bad news?' Conrad's voice broke into her thoughts and, glancing at him quickly, she shook her head.

'It's a letter from Hilary.'

He seemed pleased. 'How are they?'

'They're well,' she replied casually. 'They send their regards.'

Conrad nodded his thanks while relighting his pipe, and Vicky regarded him closely for a few seconds.

'There's a postscript to this letter which is intended for you,' she said quietly as he struck another match and held it to the bowl of his pipe. Without hesitation she read it out to him and instantly felt him stiffen beside her, his movements jerky as he flung the match away frim him. 'What wedding present did Sam give you?'

'It was nothing,' he replied, getting to his feet and in the act of walking away from her.

'Conrad!'

He stopped in his stride but did not turn around. 'It was nothing important.'

Vicky walked towards him. 'Then why the mystery?'

'If you must know,' he said impatiently over his shoulder, 'it was a handful of confetti in my suitcase.'

'Oh.' Vicky felt slightly deflated and could not think why. What had she expected?

Conrad was striding away from her and Vicky hurried to catch up with him. 'Conrad?'

'Yes, what is it now?'

She was slightly out of breath when she reached him and she stood for a moment not knowing how to phrase her next words. His scowl of impatience, however, motivated her and, taking a deep breath, she plunged into her speech.

'Hilary sent me a cheque for eight hundred Rand. Sam sold my furniture for me and,' she extracted the cheque from the envelope and held it out to him, 'I would like you to have it.'

Conrad stared at the cheque and then at her, his expression anything but encouraging. 'Are you hoping to shorten your stay here at Duiwelspoort in this way?'

Vicky shook her head. 'No. It's to compensate in some small way for the loss you suffered through my stupidity.' She swallowed at the constriction in her throat. 'I'm sorry I left the gates open the other day, Conrad.'

Conrad's face became a cold mask of disapproval, his eyes rendering her speechless as they raked over her. 'I don't want your money,' he said abruptly, turning on his heel and entering the house.

Vicky followed him quickly, their footsteps echoing through the hallway and along the passage to his study. She hesitated a moment in the doorway and then followed him in.

'Conrad, won't you please take this cheque?' she persisted, and the next moment her eyes widened with fright as he turned on her and gripped her shoulders painfully. He shook her until it seemed her neck would snap.

'What do you think I am?' he demanded harshly. 'Do you think I'm the kind of man who would accept money from a woman?'

'Conrad, please!' she begged, tears smarting her eyes. 'You're—you're hurting me!'

He released her instantly and she fell back against the door. She rubbed her shoulders gently where his cruel fingers had bitten into her soft flesh, and bitterness engulfed her.

'Do you think I have no pride, Conrad?' she asked angrily, biting down hard on her trembling lip. 'Do you think I found it easy asking you to lend me five thousand Rand? Do you realise what a blow it was to my own pride to have to ask a stranger to help me out of my difficulties?' Conrad started to say something, but she did not give him the opportunity to continue. 'No, I don't suppose you'll ever realise how degraded I felt that I had to go to such lengths. You'll never realise what it's like to be driven by fear and anxiety to do something which is so totally against your principles that every time you think of it you can only feel disgust for yourself, and you wonder how you will be able to live with yourself when the mere thought of your actions eats away at your insides until you want to shrivel up and die with shame.'

'Vicky, listen to me——'

'No, you listen to me!' Her eyes were burning with anger as she faced him. 'It was bad enough asking you to lend me that money, but I had no intention of sponging on you further. I've meticulously avoided using the allowance you've given me, although I was forced to buy myself a few things for the winter. I intended to replace the amount I spent whenever this cheque arrived, but now—now I've allowed your best stud ram to be killed and this cheque may not even cover that loss. Oh, Conrad, if I could set my pride aside to ask you for five thousand Rand, can't you do the same and accept this small cheque from me?' Her voice quivered pleadingly. 'Is it too much to ask?'

They faced each other in silence for a moment before Conrad turned from her and fished his pipe from his pocket, clenching it between his teeth without lighting it.

'I'm not an insensitive fool, Vicky. I have some idea of what it cost you to ask me for that loan, but losing one ram won't make me a pauper.'

'I don't understand.'

'My dear, in one night I've lost thirty to forty sheep. A truck is backed up against my fence, a platform is lowered, and the sheep are simply herded on to it and driven away.'

'You mean they're stolen?'

He nodded. 'The loss of thirty to forty sheep, some of them ewes about to lamb, is far greater than the loss of one ram.'

'But you were so angry and upset.'

Conrad bent to retrieve her letter and the cheque where they had fallen on the floor at her feet during his assault on her. He held them out to her.

'Of course I was angry and upset. Wouldn't you be if someone deliberately disobeyed your instructions?'

'It wasn't deliberate,' Vicky replied honestly, taking the envelope and cheque from him with unsteady fingers.

'I know that now,' his reply was more gentle. 'I won't accept your cheque, Vicky, but I shan't forget that you offered it so generously.'

Vicky turned swiftly, hiding the tears that sprang unbidden to her eyes.

'Vicky,' his voice stopped her. 'You've ridden Teresa only once since your arrival. She is there for you to use whenever you feel inclined. The stable boy will help you saddle her and if you feel nervous at the thought of riding alone, I'll arrange for Jim to go with you. He's an excellent teacher.'

Her whispered 'thank you' barely reached his ears as she wrenched open the door and fled to her room, the tears running freely down her cheeks. She could take his anger and cold indifference to a certain extent, but his gentle kindness stripped her of every defence and touched her more deeply than she would ever let him guess.

Vicky made use of Conrad's offer that same day. She rested briefly after lunch and then hurried to the stables to have Teresa saddled. The mare was placid-natured and Vicky was not at all nervous and, remembering all Conrad's instructions, she set off to where she knew he would be working on a windmill.

It was an exhilarating feeling to have the wind whistling past her, brushing against her cheeks and staining them pink. On a small rise Vicky stopped for a moment, her eyes alight with pleasure, her lips parted slightly in a smile as she noticed Conrad in the distance. She was on the verge of spurring on her mount when she noticed a chestnut mare vaulting a fence at breakneck speed and galloping toward where Conrad was perched on top of the windmill. It could only be Natalie, Vicky realised as she saw her long black hair streaming out behind her.

Conrad, too, saw her approach and quickly he climbed down to the ground, catching hold of the mare's bridle. Vicky watched Natalie bend down to speak to him, her hand clutching at his shoulder and then, with a brief nod, Conrad untethered his horse and moments later they rode off in the direction from which Natalie had come.

Vicky swallowed her disappointment. Whatever it was that Natalie had come about, it was obviously urgent, judging by the haste with which Conrad had accompanied her. Illness, perhaps? Vicky sighed and continued her solitary ride. Conrad would probably telephone if it was anything serious, she decided, putting the entire episode from her mind as swiftly as possible.

By six o'clock that evening there was still no sign of Conrad, and no word either as to what time he could be expected. Michael had come in, showered and changed, and still Vicky delayed dinner in the hope that Conrad would soon be home. By seven o'clock Vicky was more angry than worried and said as much to Lizzie on one of her frequent trips to the kitchen.

'This is really too much!' she fumed. 'He could at least have had the decency to let us know of his intentions.'

'Why doesn't the Madam phone and find out what's going on?' Lizzie suggested helpfully, viewing the dinner with concern.

'No! I have no intention of making a fool of myself.' Vicky paced the floor restlessly. 'Oh, how could he be so inconsiderate!'

'Master Conrad is used to coming and going as he pleases.'

'Well, not any more!' Vicky retorted angrily. 'He's married now, and has a wife to consider. When he feels like hopping off somewhere and remaining there for hours, the least he could do is inform me to that effect.'

Michael sauntered into the kitchen. 'I'm hungry. When are we eating?'

'That settles it!' Vicky stamped her foot angrily. 'Dish up, Lizzie. We're eating, and to the devil with Conrad!'

Lizzie smiled and nodded. 'I'll dish up Master Conrad's dinner and leave it in the oven, Madam.'

'I couldn't care less whether you fed it to the dogs,' Vicky announced, and Lizzie's chuckle followed her as she marched out of the kitchen with Michael in tow.

The angry silence lengthened after Lizzie had served them with their dinner.

'What's going on?' Michael wanted to know. 'Where's Conrad?'

'I suspect he's next door at the van Buuren place.'

'What's he doing there?'

'How should I know?' she retorted angrily. 'Natalie came dashing over on that chestnut mare of hers, and Conrad just dropped everything and went off with her.'

'She's always here,' Michael said, scowling at his food.

'What do you mean?'

'Just what I said. Natalie van Buuren is always here lately. She comes riding along and then she and Conrad laugh and chat together. One would swear they were in love with each other.'

'Michael!'

He glanced at her apologetically. 'I'm sorry, Vicky.'

Vicky pushed her food about in her plate. 'Does she really come here that often?' she asked eventually.

'Almost every day.'

Vicky stared distastefully at the plate of food before her and pushed it aside, unable to eat another mouthful.

Later, after helping Lizzie clear the table, Vicky went through to the living-room and found Michael waiting for her. 'I guess you could do with some company?'

Vicky smiled at him gratefully. 'If you're not too tired.'

It was not often that Michael joined Conrad and herself in the living-room in the evenings. He usually made some excuse and went to his room, leaving them alone together. Conrad usually buried himself behind the newspaper while Vicky busied herself with embroidery. Quite often he would go straight to his study, then Vicky would retire to her room where she would lie awake for hours before eventually falling asleep. On those occasions she hardly ever heard Conrad coming into his room, and she suspected that he remained in his study until long after midnight. When Vicky awoke in the mornings, Conrad had already left his room, the crumpled sheets and the stale smell of pipe tobacco the only evidence that he had been there.

She had taken it upon herself to make their beds and

106

tidy their rooms, hating the idea that Lizzie and her niece should speculate about the peculiar behaviour of their employer and his wife.

Michael sat slumped in a chair, his eyes half closed with fatigue. His face and arms had acquired a tan from the long hours in the sun, but despite this he looked unhappy.

'You're not happy here, are you, Michael?' she asked sympathetically, and Michael raised his heavy eyelids to meet her glance.

'I'm fed up with it all,' he said fiercely, and somehow everything came tumbling out. 'I'm sorry, Vicky. Conrad is your husband, but I'm sick to death of the way he treats me. I get all the dirty jobs to do while he and Jim do the cushy ones. It's not fair, I tell you. It's Michael do this; Michael do that; and all this leaves him free to flirt with that—that silly little girl next door!'

'Michael, I can't allow you to say these things,' Vicky protested, but she had to admit to herself that it was a half-hearted attempt at showing some loyalty to Conrad. Her husband!

Michael sat forward in his chair, his young face an earnest plea for understanding.

'Vicky, can't I go back to the city? I've learnt my lesson, and I swear I shall never do anything so stupid again. Won't you speak to Conrad for me?'

Vicky's tender heart ached with pity for him. 'The agreement was that you remained until the loan was repaid,' she reminded him gently.

'I can't stay another month longer!' he exclaimed loudly. 'It would kill me! I'm not a farmer. I'm not used to this sort of life, and I don't intend to become used to it either.'

'Conrad won't listen to me. Besides, how do you intend repaying him the five thousand Rand?'

'I'll pay it back somehow.' He fished in his pocket for his cigarettes and lit one. 'Just speak to Conrad on my

107

behalf. Please, Vicky. Do this for me, please?'

'I'll try,' she sighed, but she could have given him Conrad's answer without further trouble.

'You're the best sister a chap can have,' he remarked, kissing her on her cheek, and Vicky's lips twisted into a semblance of a smile.

Michael remained a while longer and then, unable to keep awake, he excused himself and went off to bed, leaving Vicky alone by the fire with her thoughts.

Where was Conrad? What was he doing? Why had he not sent a message to the effect that he would be late? A terrible thought came to her suddenly. Was someone ill? Otto? Sonia? Perhaps Rodney? And here she was fussing and fuming because she had not heard from Conrad. Oh, damn the man! He could have telephoned!

It was past eleven when Vicky heard the kitchen door open and close, and Conrad's heavy footsteps coming down the passage. She waited for him, the magazine she had been reading lying forgotten on her lap. Her heartbeats quickened as he appeared in the doorway.

'Hello? Not in bed yet?'

She was vaguely aware that he looked tired and drawn, but her anger drove all other thoughts from her mind.

'Where have you been?'

'At the van Buuren farm.' He frowned. 'But you know that.'

'Do I?' she asked sarcastically, and then her anger bristled as she saw his eyes flicker with amusement.

'Are you about to display a few wifely tantrums?'

'Conrad, this is no time for joking!'

'I agree with you,' he replied, turning to leave. 'It's time for bed.'

'Conrad!' He stopped in the doorway and turned, his face once again a polite mask. 'Why didn't you let me know you would be spending the evening with the van Buurens?'

'I didn't spend the evening with them, as you put it,' he told her patiently. 'I was helping——'

'Was someone ill?' she interrupted, her anger departing swiftly as concern swept through her. 'Is that why you stayed there all this time?'

Conrad's eyes narrowed and Vicky threw the magazine aside and went to him. 'I'm sorry, Conrad, if someone is ill and I've been sitting here fussing about trivial things.'

Conrad looked down at her from his great height, his eyes intent upon her face. 'Didn't Natalie telephone you?'

'Should she have?' Vicky asked cautiously, and then she knew with sharp clarity what had happened. Conrad had asked Natalie to telephone her and Natalie, for some reason, had not done so.

Conrad confirmed her suspicions by saying, 'I asked Natalie to telephone you early this evening, but the little devil obviously didn't. I'm sorry, Vicky. One of their cows was in labour and they could see that she was having some difficulty. It was just as well that they called me or they might have lost the cow as well as her calf.'

His clothes were dirty and there was blood on his shirt sleeve, Vicky noticed for the first time as her anger evaporated completely.

'I was—worried,' she admitted grudgingly, her eyes downcast.

'I realise that, and I'm sorry.'

Vicky drew a deep breath. 'I suppose you've eaten, but could I make you a cup of coffee perhaps?'

He glanced down ruefully at his clothes. 'Would you mind if I had a shower first?'

'I'll have the coffee waiting here for you when you return,' she told him, her thoughts in turmoil.

She was in no hurry while she made the coffee, giving

him ample time to have his shower and to return to the living-room. She could not suppress the feeling of pleasure that surged through her at the thought that Conrad had at least not forgotten her existence. He *had* thought to send her a message, even though it was never delivered. Why, she wondered suddenly, had Natalie not telephoned? Had she merely forgotten, or was it deliberate? She shrugged off these thoughts as she heard the shower being turned off, and quickly she set the cups in a tray and poured their coffee. This was actually quite an occasion, she thought to herself as she carried the tray to the living-room, for she and Conrad had never yet had coffee together at this hour of the night.

Vicky felt her heart lurch when Conrad entered the room moments later. He looked decidedly boyish in his blue silk dressing-gown with his dark hair still damp from the shower and combed back severely. His chin was clean-shaven and he smelled delightfully of after-shave lotion. His striped pyjama pants protruded below his gown, but she could see that he wore no top, for his gown was open almost to the waist, displaying the dark hair on his tanned, muscular chest.

He sat down in his usual chair by the fire and Vicky handed him his coffee. Their fingers touched briefly and Vicky's pulse quickened. They sat in companionable silence drinking their coffee and Vicky's thoughts drifted to the conversation she had had with Michael earlier that evening. Perhaps now was the right moment to speak to Conrad, she decided, yet she could not bring herself to broach the subject. She glanced across at him and saw him staring down at his unlit pipe in his hand, almost as if he had no idea what to do with it.

Vicky's heart softened curiously. To mention Michael's problems at that moment would disturb the air of tranquillity between them, and yet she knew that Michael

110

would expect some sort of answer the following day. The moments ticked by as she sat there torn between the desire to help Michael, and the sure knowledge that this time her brother would have to pay the full price for his foolish actions.

'Conrad,' she began hesitantly, 'about Michael.'

Conrad clenched his pipe between his teeth, and waited. Vicky watched him light his pipe and when he had done so, she continued, 'He's not very happy here.'

'I'm not surprised.'

'He—he wants to go back to the city.'

'Does he?' Conrad asked a trifle drily. 'You realise of course that he can't go?'

'Yes, I do,' she admitted, lowering her glance. 'If he should become involved with his old friends it wouldn't be long before he found himself in the same position as before.'

Conrad nodded, sucking at his pipe with his eyes half closed. 'There's another reason why he can't leave here. The authorities would probably not have allowed the Atlas Company to withdraw their case against him if he had not placed himself in my custody.'

'I know.'

'But?' he looked at her quizzically. 'There is a but, I presume?'

Vicky took a deep breath. 'Don't you think you're driving him a little too hard?'

'No, I don't think so.' The muscles in his jaw hardened as he clamped his teeth on to the stem of his pipe. 'The trouble with Michael is that he can't take discipline, and you must admit that there's been a curious lack of disciplinary measures in his young life.'

'Conrad, I——'

'I'm not blaming you, Vicky,' he interrupted swiftly, 'but your leniency towards him certainly didn't help much to correct this error. Did it?'

'No.' Her heart was thudding heavily against her ribs. It was true, she had spoilt Michael. She had given in to his every whim because he was her little brother, and because she loved him.

'I suppose Michael has been talking to you?'

The question came so suddenly that Vicky could not hide the truth from him. 'Yes, he did mention something about wishing he could return to the city.'

The silence that followed was almost unbearable and Vicky sat wringing her hands nervously in her lap, conscious only of Conrad's brooding silence as he sat facing her, and her own helplessness and inadequacy.

'Do you trust me to do my best for Michael?' Conrad asked quietly, and Vicky's hands stilled in her lap.

Did she trust Conrad? Did he actually have Michael's interests at heart, or was he merely demanding repayment of money loaned? No! No, Conrad was not like that, her subconscious rejected the idea. He understood Michael better than she had given him credit for, and he was obviously an excellent judge of character. Michael did need discipline and Conrad, she had to admit, was the right man to administer it.

'I—I seem to have helped him make a mess of his life,' she replied tremulously. 'I would be grateful if you could salvage something out of this whole sordid business.'

'Sordid?' he frowned slightly. 'That's rather a strong word, Vicky. I would rather use the word "unfortunate". Would you say that being married to me and living here at Duiwelspoort is sordid?'

'No, I——' She bit her lip to steady it. 'That's not what I meant, Conrad. I was referring to Michael and ... and what he did,' she ended lamely, staring into the dying embers of the fire.

Conrad rose to his feet and walked across to the fireplace. He, too, stood staring down at it as though there

112

was something there he found vastly interesting.

'Vicky, are you happy here, or do you find it lonely?'

'I don't find it lonely at all.'

'Do you miss your friends?'

'I miss Hilary. We were very close.'

'You still haven't answered the first part of my question,' Conrad remarked, his back towards her. 'Are you happy here?'

By what does one measure happiness? she thought. If one was searching for it, what would one look for? And, if she was unhappy, what was the cause of it? Could one always pinpoint the little things that made one unhappy?

Conrad turned and Vicky met his questioning glance steadily. 'I love your home and the garden, and I don't find life away from the city at all repulsive.' She laughed shakily. 'I must admit, though, that I feel like an intruder.'

'But you're my wife, and this is your home as much as mine!'

His wife for a year! A year during which she was to think of his home as her own, and afterwards . . . ? An involuntary sigh escaped her as she averted her gaze.

'I would like you to think of Duiwelspoort as your home,' she heard him say. 'I want you to feel free to do whatever you want in the house without the feeling that you should ask my permission.'

'Thank you, Conrad. You're very kind.'

For a brief moment their glances locked, then Conrad turned away and Vicky hastily removed the cups to the kitchen. She rinsed them and left them in the rack to dry. It was long past midnight, she noticed as she turned out the lights and returned to the living-room. Conrad was still there, slumped in a chair, his pipe clenched between his teeth.

Vicky hesitated in the doorway. 'Goodnight, Conrad.'

He removed his pipe and rose to his feet. 'Goodnight, Vicky. Sleep well.'

His eyes had that same penetrating quality as on the first occasion they had met, and Vicky was all at once aware of the clamouring of her heart and a strange weakness in her limbs that made them refuse to do her bidding. She stood motionless, unable to tear her glance away from his.

'Vicky?'

He moved then, closing the gap between them until she had to crane her neck to look up at him.

'I—I don't understand,' she said thickly, her eyes dark and questioning. 'Whatever it is, it frightens me because I don't understand.'

She hardly knew what she was saying, and was quite unaware that she was speaking her thoughts aloud. Conrad's hands, warm and rough, were framing her face and his eyes were looking down into her own.

'Don't let it trouble you, Vicky,' he whispered. Then he was gone.

Vicky could not sleep that night. She spent the hours tossing in bed and wishing for the dawn. Conrad, apparently, was just as restless, for, long after the strip of light had disappeared beneath his door, she could still hear him moving about. Was he just as troubled as she? Vicky pummelled her pillows and rolled over. What was the matter with her? What had happened to the level-headed woman she had been just a few months ago? What was it that was making her so unsure of herself? On certain occasions she felt certain that the answer was within her grasp, and then it faded to leave her even more puzzled than before.

Duiwelspoort was now her home, Conrad had said. Would he, she wondered, tell his second wife of the time he had been married before? Would he tell her, in detail, about the year they had spent together? Perhaps laugh together over little incidents which he had found amusing? For instance, her own reactions to his kisses?

Vicky groaned and turned her face into the pillow. If only this night would end, to bring relief from the punishment of her own thoughts! Endless, torturing hours dragged by, and as a glimmer of light appeared in the east, Vicky slipped into an exhausted sleep, her corn-coloured hair spread out across the pillow, her eyelashes damp with unshed tears.

CHAPTER SEVEN

SHEARING time loomed ahead with the approach of spring, and Vicky could hardly believe that three months had passed since her arrival at Duiwelspoort. She spent an enormous amount of time these days exploring the farm on horseback, and on one of these trips she had discovered a delightful pool close to a windmill where the willow and blue-gum trees would give adequate shade during the summer months. On questioning Lizzie about her discovery, she was told that it would be quite safe to swim there when the weather was warmer.

'It is a natural pool that was used as a drinking place for the sheep,' Lizzie had told her. 'Master Conrad's father planted the trees to give the sheep enough shade because it can get hot here in the Karroo in the summer. Later when Master Conrad and Miss Barbara started using the pool as a place to swim, Master Conrad's father fenced it off and built troughs instead where the sheep could drink.'

'But there's no gate,' Vicky had protested.

'That's right, Madam, but the fence used to run along the bottom end of the pool, and it now runs between the pool and the windmill. There is still enough shade for the sheep and instead of drinking water from the pool, they drink out of troughs.'

Despite herself Vicky began to look forward to spending the summer at Duiwelspoort as she contemplated the added attraction of the pool she had come upon so unexpectedly. Would Conrad object? she wondered. But then why should he?

Rodney van Buuren had become a constant visitor at

Duiwelspoort and quite often went riding with Vicky, giving her confidence in the new-found pleasure of her outings with Teresa. She was also well aware of the fact that Conrad's brooding glances had followed them as they set out on these excursions, and it gave her a curious joy to pay him back in some small measure for the times she had seen him riding off in Natalie's vivacious company. Let him brood about her friendship with Rodney, she had thought laughingly. It was, after all, nothing more than friendship between herself and Natalie's brother, and although at times he embarrassed her by asking too many personal questions, she usually managed to evade them by steering the conversation in a different direction.

There was one occasion she remembered vividly when they had tethered their horses to a tree on a small rise and seated themselves on a fallen tree trunk. She was flushed from her ride, and her hair had been loosened by the wind.

'I don't think I should come here so often in the future,' Rodney had remarked. 'I'm in love with you. You know that, don't you?'

Vicky had looked away, out across the veld to where Michael and Jim were herding the sheep into a camp. Yes, she had known that Rodney was in love with her; she had guessed it some time ago, and yet she could not bring herself to break off their friendship. She was fond of him. He filled her lonely hours, and selfishly she had ignored the signs of his growing affection and had allowed him to call on her whenever he had wished.

'I'm sorry, Rodney,' she whispered. 'It's my fault really.'

He gripped her hands tightly. 'Don't say that! You've given me absolutely no encouragement, and I have only myself to blame.' He appraised her tenderly and with some envy. 'I wonder if Conrad realises how lucky he is. If you were my wife, Vicky, I would never let you out of my sight for fear of someone whisking you off when I wasn't around.'

'Don't be silly,' Vicky laughed.

'It's true, though,' he insisted, glancing at her thoughtfully. 'Are you happy, Vicky?'

Vicky's heart lurched. Everyone seemed so terribly concerned about her happiness. First it was Hilary's letter, to which she had replied with carefully fabricated lies that had sickened her, saying that she had insisted on Michael coming with her seeing that he was still young and unstable; secondly Conrad had asked her the same thing, and she had evaded giving him a direct reply. Now it was Rodney, and she knew somehow that he would not be as easily fooled as the others.

'Why should you be so concerned about my happiness?' she asked casually, attempting to laugh off the question.

'I think perhaps because you deserve to be happy.'

She glanced at him sharply. 'How does one deserve happiness? Isn't happiness to be found in the things you see around you? In the smell of the earth, the bleating of a lamb as it searches for its mother, the sight of a calf as it nuzzles up to the cow and drinks its fill, or the tangy smell of the Karroo bush when it's wet with dew. Oh, yes,' she continued as he raised his eyebrows, 'I've walked in the veld in the early morning while the sun was struggling to disperse the chill of the night, and I've inhaled the fragrance of this fantastic little bush you all love so much.' She smiled up at Rodney. 'Isn't this all part of happiness?'

Vicky knew that she would never forget the look in Rodney's eyes at that moment. He knew that she had once again smartly evaded his question, and he must have sensed that something was wrong between herself and Conrad. He knew it as surely as Hilary had known it, and Vicky hated herself for the deception.

'Forgive me for asking this, Vicky,' Rodney had asked, avoiding her eyes. 'Did you marry Conrad for his money?'

Vicky felt as though a douche of cold water had been

dashed into her face. She had undeniably married Conrad for his money, but not in the way Rodney was suggesting.

'You ask me that as though—as though Conrad was an extremely wealthy man,' she said haltingly, her nerves taut.

Rodney turned to her then in amazement. 'But didn't you know?'

'Know what, for goodness' sake?'

'Conrad is one of the wealthiest farmers in the district.'

Vicky could never remember afterwards exactly what she had replied to this statement, she knew only that she had ridden back to the homestead that day in stunned silence while she had digested this information. It was no wonder Rodney had asked her that question, and she wondered how many others had arrived at the same conclusion, that she had married Conrad exclusively for his money.

There had been a sickening feeling at the pit of her stomach as she and Rodney had parted company that day, and the feeling remained with her for some time.

Michael's attitude remained the same towards Conrad. It caused endless moments of tension and stress, and quite often they came perilously close to blows. Vicky's intervention on those occasions only served to bring further strain on her relationship with Conrad, who accused her of pampering Michael so much that he was becoming a rebel.

'You're not being fair,' she had accused Conrad one evening when they were alone in the living-room. 'You're driving him beyond his endurance. He isn't physically capable of doing the things you expect of him, and neither has he your knowledge.'

'Physically he is capable of doing far more than you'll give him credit for, and knowledge is something which could be acquired if he applied himself,' Conrad had replied angrily. 'You've pampered him long enough, Vicky. He's no longer a child, and if he was man enough to think up

119

his fraudulent actions, then he is man enough to atone for them.'

'I think you're cruel and heartless!'

Conrad's white face had frightened her. 'Cruel and heartless, am I? I'll show you just how cruel and heartless I can be!'

The pressure of his lips and hands had been an agony she would not forget easily, and the bruises on the soft flesh of her upper arms had acted as a reminder for some time afterwards and effectively silenced her on other occasions when Michael displayed his temperament.

Vicky awoke one morning with the exhilarating feeling that only spring could instil. The September sun rose in the cloudless sky, and from her window she could see the birds fluttering about the bird bath in the garden. In the camp beyond the garden, the ewes were grazing with their lambs, while on the lawn below, Caesar and Cleo were romping, snapping at each other and rolling on the dewy grass.

Opening her window further, she called down to them and they stopped their playful game instantly to glance up at her, their tails wagging.

She inhaled the cool fresh air, drawing it deep into her lungs. 'Do you feel it too?' she called to them. 'Are you also aware of the springy feeling in the air?'

Caesar and Cleo barked up at her and she laughed joyously.

'They obviously understood what you were saying.'

Vicky swung round sharply to see Conrad standing in the communicating door. Embarrassingly conscious of the transparency of her attire, she made a dive for the warm woollen robe at the foot of her bed and slipped into it hastily, tightening the cord about her waist.

'You could have knocked,' she accused, unable to meet his glance.

'I did, but you obviously never heard me.'

Her heart was hammering uncomfortably against her ribs. 'Did you want something?'

'What would you do if I said yes ... I want you?'

Vicky's head shot up. Her heart stopped, and then raced on at a suffocating speed as she stared at him. He came towards her and she backed away involuntarily.

'Don't be alarmed,' he laughed mockingly. 'I don't usually make love to women when they show quite plainly that they aren't interested.'

'You speak as though you've had experience,' Vicky remarked, a leaden feeling in her chest.

'I'm thirty-eight, Vicky, and I'm human.'

'Have there been—many?'

'A few,' he laughed. 'Does it shock you?'

Vicky clasped her trembling hands behind her back, the muscles in her throat tightening. 'It's none of my business.'

There was a significant pause. 'You're right,' Conrad said bluntly. 'It's none of your business.'

Again there was that tense silence. 'What did—did you want to see me about?'

'I'm going to town. Would you like to come too?'

'Yes. Yes, I would.'

He glanced at his watch. 'I'll give you thirty minutes to get ready. We'll have breakfast and leave immediately afterwards.'

As the communicating door closed behind him, Vicky swallowed violently at the lump in her throat and dashed into the bathroom. Thirty minutes later, bathed and dressed, she sat down to breakfast with him in the dining-room.

Conrad glanced at his watch and smiled approvingly. 'That's another characteristic I like in my women. Punctuality and obedience.'

'Oh, shut up!'

'Ah! And they must be spirited as well.'

Vicky glared at him. 'Don't try to be more insufferable than you already are, Conrad.'

'I'm just mentioning a few of the——'

'Yes, I know,' she interrupted bitterly. 'A few of the characteristics you like your—women to have.'

'Exactly,' he bowed his head mockingly in her direction.

'Well, I'm not one of your—women!' she replied hotly.

'You are, you know,' he replied, quite unperturbed. 'You're number one woman in this household, and I have a certificate to prove it.'

'I think you're ...' She hesitated and bit her lip.

'Despicable?' he filled in for her, his lips twisted with cynicism. 'Yes, perhaps I am, but then you usually provoke me.'

Vicky stared at him aghast. 'I provoke you? I've never yet provoked you!'

'Oh, yes, you have, and you do.'

'You always taunt me,' she snapped back.

'Not taunt, my dear,' he shook his head. 'Tease, yes, but not taunt.'

'Why should you want to tease me?'

Conrad shrugged and applied himself to the bacon and eggs on his plate. 'I tease you mainly because I like to see you blush, and the way your eyes sparkle when you're angry.'

To her horror she felt her cheeks go scarlet, and Conrad, glancing up at that moment, burst out laughing.

'You see? You're blushing, and your eyes are sparkling with anger because you know that what I've said is the truth.'

Never in her life had she felt so like striking anyone, and she clenched her hands in her lap. 'If I were a man ...' she hissed through her teeth.

'Darling, you're not a man,' he smiled at her. 'You're the

most delectable, delightful female I have ever met. Now eat your breakfast, it's getting late.'

Vicky bit back a retort and forced herself instead to eat a little of the breakfast Lizzie had prepared.

The trip into town was not as unpleasant as Vicky had feared. As they drove down the main street he asked: 'Where would you like me to drop you off?'

'At the chemist will do.'

'Are you going to buy some of that stuff you women put on your faces?'

'I don't put "stuff" on my face,' she replied indignantly. 'I use foundation, powder and lipstick.'

'Remarkable. Quite remarkable,' he teased, slowing down and swerving to the side of the street. 'How do you manage to have such a wholesome complexion?'

'Perhaps I'm just fortunate.'

Conrad turned to her and smiled sardonically as he scrutinised her. 'You're blushing again.'

'And you're impossible!' she exclaimed, feeling blindly for the door handle. 'Where shall I meet you again?'

'At the tea room, I think. In an hour's time.'

'Hello, there!'

Vicky and Conrad both glanced up to see Natalie approaching the Holden. She went round to Conrad's side and stooped slightly to glance in at the window.

'I'm glad you're in town,' she told Conrad after a brief nod in Vicky's direction. 'I've just seen the most marvellous bit of horseflesh and I would like your opinion.'

'Where is it?' Conrad asked quickly.

'At the stockyards.' Natalie's smile was sweetly innocent as she glanced past him. 'You won't mind, will you, Vicky? They're keeping it for me while I make up my mind.'

'Not at all,' Vicky replied stiffly, stepping out on to the pavement.

Conrad glanced at her swiftly. 'The tea room, Vicky? In an hour?'

'Yes, I'll be there.'

Vicky turned quickly and entered the chemist's. Through the window she saw Natalie sliding into the seat she had just vacated. She was laughing up at Conrad and his glance was equally amused. The Holden disappeared swiftly down the street and Vicky turned her attention to her purchases.

The town was not exceptionally busy and Vicky, carrying her few parcels, arrived at the tea room ten minutes before time. She selected a table close to the door and refrained from placing an order, expecting Conrad to arrive at any moment. Fifteen minutes passed ... twenty ... thirty! Where was Conrad? The waitress hovered about, darting curious glances in her direction, and still Vicky waited.

The minutes ticked by and a slow anger churned inside her. What kind of a fool did he think she was? Presumably time meant nothing to him when he was with Natalie and everyone else could just wait!

The waitress hovered about once more and this time Vicky ordered a pot of tea. To the devil with Conrad and Natalie!

Twenty minutes later Conrad entered the tea room and walked across to her with his long, slow strides. 'Vicky, I'm sorry——'

'Oh, please don't apologise, Conrad,' she interrupted sarcastically. 'I've spent a most enjoyable hour enduring the curious glances of the staff.'

'Vicky!' he hissed, his glance ominous.

Vicky smiled up at him for the benefit of the onlookers, but her voice was filled with chilling anger. 'Did you find it so difficult to tear yourself away from Natalie?'

'Natalie had nothing to do with it!'

'Really?' She raised her eyebrows and gestured towards

the tea-pot. 'The tea is cold, but I suppose I could order another pot if you think you could bear to be seen with me.'

'Have you quite finished?'

Vicky met his cold glance. 'Yes, Conrad. I'm quite finished.'

'Good. Let's go.'

The drive home was completed in an angry silence, except when he instructed her to slide in behind the wheel so that he could open the gates. In the driveway Jim ran to meet them, his expression clearly troubled.

'Oh, lord, what now?' Conrad groaned, jumping out and going to meet him.

'Master Michael has gone,' she heard Jim say, and a cold chill of fear gripped her.

'He's what?' Conrad exploded.

'He packed his things and left in the small truck,' Jim explained, glancing apologetically at Vicky as she approached them.

'Why in the name of heaven didn't you stop him?' Conrad demanded.

'He was gone before we realised what he meant to do, Master Conrad,' Jim apologised. 'I'm sorry.'

Conrad's chest heaved slightly. 'It's all right, Jim. I understand. You may go.'

Jim hurried away and Vicky turned to Conrad. 'I—I'm sorry.'

'Did you know about this?'

She saw the cold fury in his face and took an involuntary step backwards. 'No! I had no idea.'

'And if you had I suppose you wouldn't have told me!'

'Conrad, I——' Her eyes widened suddenly as he strode towards the Holden. 'Where are you going?'

'I'm going to find him and I'm going to bring him back here if it's the last thing I do.'

'I'm coming with you,' she said quickly, getting in beside him even as he started the engine.

Conrad made no reply, but the look of grim determination on his face frightened her. She had never seen him so angry and she was suddenly terribly afraid for Michael if they should catch up with him.

It was a nightmare journey for Vicky. Conrad drove fast and furiously and Vicky clung to her seat, closing her eyes at times and praying softly to herself. At this speed they would be lucky if they arrived at Koelenberg alive, she thought, her heart lurching violently with fear as the Holden skidded around a bend. Conrad slowed down in town; then, as they passed the station, he slammed on the brakes so suddenly that Vicky was thrown forward against the dashboard, saving herself from serious injury by holding out her hands protectively.

'There's my truck!' Conrad said tersely, sliding from his seat and entering the station building. He emerged a few minutes later and slid behind the wheel. 'He's on a train bound for Cape Town. Fortunately it's the slow train that stops at every little siding on the way.'

'Are you going to try and catch up with it?' she asked in disbelief.

'I'm not just going to try,' he remarked, his lips drawn into a thin line. 'I'm going to! So hold on to your seat.'

The nightmare continued and seemed to last for hours as Conrad followed the route of the train.

'Conrad, you'll kill us both if you continue like this!' she cried as the Holden skidded around another bend.

'I didn't ask you to come with me.'

'But I had to. He's my brother and I——' she bit her lip, unable to continue.

'You're frightened of what I might do?' he guessed expertly.

'Yes.' She glanced at him quickly. 'You're beside yourself with anger at the moment.'

Conrad's expression hardened even more. 'I'm going to teach that brother of yours a lesson he'll never forget—that's what I'm going to do. And I don't want any interference from you, is that clear?'

Vicky thought it best not to reply and maintained an absolute silence until, mercifully, the train was in sight. They reached the small siding before the train, but the instant it stopped Conrad was out of the Holden and speaking to the guard, who had alighted. Moments later she saw them walking further along the train to where the guard was evidently directing Conrad, and with fast-beating heart she saw him disappear into one of the carriages.

Endless minutes seemed to pass before she saw Michael emerge with a suitcase in his hand and Conrad close behind him. Conrad said something to the guard and then Michael was climbing into the back seat of the Holden, dumping his suitcase on the floor beside him. His scowling face was a mixture of anger and uncertainty, and Vicky smiled at him encouragingly although her own heart was heavy-laden.

The journey back to Duiwelspoort was not as reckless as the chase had been and, if for nothing else, Vicky was thankful for that. At the Koelenberg station Conrad stopped to pick up the truck, instructing Vicky to drive ahead, which she did gratefully. It would at least give her a few minutes with Michael.

'Why did you do it?' she asked in an anguished voice.

'I—I was tired of taking instructions from Conrad, and tired of being shunted around. I wanted to—to get away.'

It was the first time Vicky had ever hard Michael stammer. He had always been so sure of himself; so certain about what he wanted, and what he wanted to do.

'You realise, of course, that Conrad is very angry,' she

127

reminded him gently, 'and I think this time he has reason to be.'

She met his glance in the rear view mirror and he nodded, glancing away quickly, but not before she had seen him swallow convulsively.

'Oh, Michael,' she sighed shakily. 'Why couldn't you discipline yourself to stay put? It's not for a lifetime.'

Michael gestured wildly. 'How can I stay when I know that Conrad hates me?'

'Hates you?' she gasped incredulously. 'But that's ridiculous! Conrad doesn't hate you!'

'He does! He despises me because of what I did!'

Further conversation was impossible, for the gates of Duiwelspoort were ahead of them and Michael jumped out smartly each time to open them so that the two vehicles could pass through. Conrad took the truck around the side of the house to the shed where he kept his lorries while Vicky and Michael waited rather tensely for him to reappear.

The moment Vicky dreaded drew near as Conrad came striding towards them, his expression thunderous.

'You and I are going for a walk, Michael,' he said angrily. 'There's something I want to say to you.'

'Conrad, don't you think——' Vicky bit her lip as Conrad swung round to face her.

'I think you should leave this matter to me.' His voice was dangerously calm, and absolutely forbidding.

'What are you going to do?' she asked tremulously.

'What I'm going to do need not concern you.'

'Conrad, don't——'

'Go inside!' he said with a sudden savagery she had not heard before and, frightened, she fled into the house.

Vicky paced the living-room floor for what seemed like hours. Each time she passed the window she peered into the distance, but they were nowhere in sight. What were they doing? Or, more to the point, what was Conrad doing?

The uncertainty was killing her. If only Conrad would be able to control his anger, she thought wildly. Physically, Conrad and Michael were an ill-matched pair and if, when tempers flared, they should strike out at each other, Michael would be the one to get hurt.

Vicky continued her pacing with more urgency. The tension of waiting increased with every second. In the driveway stood the dust-covered Holden, and Vicky once again relived those moments of fear during their hair-raising dash after Michael. If Conrad had not been such an excellent driver, they would surely not have reached their destination alive, she thought with a shudder. Each time the Holden had skidded, Conrad had brought it expertly back on to the road and Vicky, with her eyes tightly closed most of the time, had sent up endless prayers for their safety.

Footsteps sounded on the gravel outside and she remained rigid in the centre of the living-room, waiting. The front door opened and closed and Vicky, unable to restrain herself, rushed into the hall, and a swift pang of fear shot through her as she stared from one to the other.

What on earth was going on? she wondered in confusion. She had more or less expected them to come to blows, she had also expected anger and resentment from Michael, and a terrifying anger from Conrad. But this? They were actually smiling at each other. What had happened to bring this remarkable change in their attitudes?

'I don't—I don't understand,' she muttered, shaking her head in helpless confusion. 'Would one of you kindly explain what's going on, if it's not too much trouble?'

'Vicky,' Michael forestalled Conrad, 'Conrad and I have decided to bury the hatchet. I admit quite freely that I've been to blame for the trouble between us, and I'm sorry. I had a twisted idea that Conrad was deliberately trying to goad me. I objected to every instruction he gave me and generally made life difficult for him. I realise now how wrong

I was.' He laughed boyishly. 'Conrad is giving me another chance to prove that I'm not as bad as I seemed.'

Vicky glanced at Conrad and he nodded as if confirming everything Michael had said. She sighed heavily, still not quite understanding the change in Michael.

Whatever it was that had happened between them that day, it marked a turning point in Vicky and Michael's stay at Duiwelspoort. For the first time he began to enjoy life on the farm and talked freely to Conrad during the evenings they spent together in the living-room. Vicky would embroider or knit, and eventually make them coffee before they all retired for the evening. Michael was at ease with Conrad, which was more than Vicky could say for herself, and their new relationship eased the tension in the home considerably.

The months slipped by with comparative ease; months during which Rodney remained a frequent visitor at Duiwelspoort. He took great care not to mention his feelings to her and Vicky, knowing this, kept their conversations casual, although a certain amount of strain crept into their friendship. Natalie, too, came to the farm quite often, yet Vicky merely caught glimpses of her, for she usually went straight to where Conrad and Michael were working. Her behaviour angered Vicky, but she felt powerless to do anything about it.

As summer approached and the days grew warmer, Vicky often rode out to the pool during her leisure hours, for a swim. No one was ever in sight and the pool was quite secluded behind the trees. She tried on those occasions to imagine Conrad as a young boy, swimming there with his sister, perhaps laughing and splashing each other as children do, or giving each other a ducking. But these were impossible thoughts, for, knowing Conrad as he was now, she could never somehow imagine him as a carefree child.

It was on a blisteringly hot summer's day towards the end of November that Vicky, on Teresa, once more found herself near the pool. She had had no intention of going for a swim and had therefore not brought her swimsuit, but the heat was oppressive and the scorching rays of the sun made the clear water appear more than inviting. After a momentary hesitation, she tethered her horse to a tree, and glanced about her swiftly, but no one was in sight as she disappeared among the trees and stripped off her clothing. Self-conscious about her nakedness, she draped her clothes over a low-hanging branch and plunged into the water. It was cool and exhilarating, and quite a new experience for Vicky to be swimming in the nude. If Hilary were to see her now she would be shocked to discover that her friend, always so prim and proper, was behaving in such an uncharacteristic fashion.

Vicky laughed at her own thoughts and swam with leisurely strokes to the other side of the pool. This was delightful, she thought to herself. Why had she never thought of doing this before? There was, after all, never anyone about to spy on her, except perhaps the birds chirping happily in the trees and the cicadas screaming in the heat.

She turned over on to her back and, to her horror, discovered that she was no longer alone. Standing with his back resting against the very tree where she had placed her clothes was Conrad, his pipe clenched between his teeth, his expression evidently amused at the sight of her flaming cheeks.

'What are you doing here?' she cried, sinking lower into the water and hating herself for her stupidity.

'I was looking for you, and I happened to see your horse tethered to the tree.'

'Go away!' she shouted, treading water and wishing she could disappear.

'Why?'

His casualness infuriated her. 'I haven't any clothes on.'

Conrad glanced at her clothes draped across the branch beside him before returning his glance to her. 'So I notice,' he remarked innocently. He pushed his pipe into the top pocket of his safari jacket and proceeded to undo the buttons. 'May I join you?'

'No!' she swallowed convulsively, watching with fascinated horror as he removed his jacket and started undoing the belt of his pants. 'For God's sake, Conrad, stop it!' she cried in a choked voice, covering her face with her hands and expecting any minute to hear him diving into the water.

'I want to talk to you,' she heard him say, not daring to remove her hands from her face. 'I have no intention of standing here shouting at you, so either I go in, or you come out.'

Vicky peered carefully through her fingers to see him standing at the water's edge, his hands on his hips and his pants still firmly in position.

'I—I'll come out,' she gulped. 'Will you turn around and promise not to look while I get dressed?'

Conrad laughed shortly. 'And if I don't?'

Vicky placed her hands against her burning cheeks, her heart beating so fast that she was almost gasping for breath. Her lips moved but no sound came as she stared at him, wide-eyed and helpless. Then he turned his back on her.

'Get out and get dressed,' he ordered over his shoulder. 'And make it snappy.'

He sat down on a fallen tree stump with his back to her and slipped on his jacket, his manner quite unconcerned as she swam to the edge with quick strokes and clambered out. Getting into her clothes while her body was still damp was more difficult than she had imagined, and his disturbing presence only made her fumble with nervous haste as she struggled to fasten the catch of her bra.

132

'Are you dressed?'

'No!' she grabbed her shirt and held it in front of her, a pulse jerking nervously in her throat. 'I—I'll tell you when you can turn around.'

Conrad sighed and lit his pipe. 'Do you always take so long to dress?' he asked in between puffs.

'I didn't bring a towel to dry myself with and it's difficult getting dressed when your body is wet.'

'How far are you now?'

'Mind your own business ... and keep your eyes to the front!' she warned sharply as he made as if to turn around.

Conrad laughed softly to himself and Vicky, hating him for placing her in this uncomfortable position, hastily pulled on her slacks and slipped into her shirt, fastening the buttons with trembling fingers.

'You can turn around now,' she said moments later, pulling the pins from her damp hair and letting it fall to her shoulders.

Conrad turned slowly to face her, his eyes moving slowly from her face down the length of her body to the comfortable shoes she wore on her feet. He raised his glance to her face once more and pointed to the space on the tree stump beside him.

'Sit down, I want to talk to you.'

Vicky pushed agitated fingers through her hair, flicking it over her shoulders.

'You sound serious,' she remarked as she sat down awkwardly beside him. He had not bothered to fasten the buttons of his jacket and his brown, muscular chest was disturbing to her pulse rate.

'This is rather serious.' His gaze rested upon her intently. 'My mother telephoned to say that she and my father would be arriving next week and that they intended staying for Christmas if we had no objection.'

'But naturally we have no objection,' Vicky said hastily,

nervous and at the same time excited at the prospect of meeting his parents once more.

Conrad said nothing for a moment as he gazed out across the pool. The branches of the willow tree dipped into the pool and swayed in the hot summer breeze, like a giant hand trailing in the water.

'You don't seem to realise what this implies,' he said slowly, avoiding her questioning glance. 'It will mean a lot more play-acting on our part, and something else we hadn't bargained for.'

Vicky sat silently beside him for a moment, and then said rather stiffly, 'You'd better tell me the worst.'

'My mother has a way of prying into things,' he explained carefully. 'She means no harm, but it can be embarrassing. For instance, she has a habit of walking through all the rooms, I think perhaps reliving the days she was mistress of this house. She loved Duiwelspoort, but my father insisted that they get right away from it so that I could carry on with the farming without his interference.' He hesitated a moment, knocking his pipe out against the tree stump. 'If she sees the single bed made up in the dressing-room she'll wonder why, and make it her business to find out.'

Vicky went cold. 'Are you suggesting that—that we——' She faltered and stopped, unable to continue as her mind leapt from one horrifying conclusion to the other.

'I'm suggesting nothing,' he stated bluntly, pocketing his pipe. 'The sheets will have to be removed from that bed during their stay. I'll have to make do with a blanket and a pillow which will have to be removed smartly every morning. Some of my possessions will have to be transferred to your room and ... I shall have to enter my room via yours each evening.'

'I—I see.'

'There is one other thing.' He glanced at her easily. 'I suggest that you use the bathroom as your dressing-room

134

during their stay. It would look silly if I had to stand outside the bedroom door, knocking and asking whether you were decent.'

Vicky blushed crimson and averted her glance. 'Do you think we'll be able to make them believe our marriage is real?'

Conrad shrugged his shoulders and got to his feet. He walked a few paces away and turned, his grey eyes regarding her intently. 'It will naturally depend entirely upon you.'

Vicky drew her breath in swiftly. 'What do you mean?'

'Your reaction to my kisses and caresses will be carefully noted by mother,' he replied calmly. 'She's waited a long time to see me married, and she will want to make sure that I'm happy.'

Vicky placed her hands against her hot cheeks. 'This is impossible!'

'Not really so impossible,' he said laughingly, taking her hands away from her face and pulling her to her feet. 'We have a week to practise.'

Vicky shrank away from him, but his grip on her wrists merely tightened. 'Conrad, please——'

'You'll have to get used to it sooner or later,' he remarked mockingly. 'Rather sooner than later I should say, or Mother might begin to suspect.'

She struggled to free herself, but he drew her relentlessly towards him, and as his arms finally closed about her, she knew that it would be futile to struggle further.

'Relax, Vicky,' he ordered with his lips brushing against hers. 'Try thinking it's someone whom you care for very much who's kissing you now, and forget that it's I.'

That was a ridiculous suggestion, she thought wildly as his lips claimed hers, for no man had ever kissed her the way Conrad was kissing her. No man, except Conrad, had ever awakened such frantic emotions by the mere touch of his hands and lips, and the surge of delight that swept through her, swiftly and alarmingly, could not be compared with her cool level-headed emotions when she had been kissed by other men.

Against her will she relaxed in his arms and allowed herself to be swept along on a tide of emotion that was not entirely in keeping with the reason for this exercise.

'Is it so terrible to be kissed by me?' he asked raising his head slightly to look into her eyes.

'No,' she breathed softly, surprising herself by making no effort to free herself.

'Shall we try again?'

'Yes,' she murmured trance-like, as she slid her arms about his neck and threaded her fingers through his crisp, dark hair.

Later, much later, his lips strayed across her cheek and down the column of her slender throat. But, as they explored lower, sanity returned with a swift rush of shame.

'This is madness!' she gasped, freeing herself from his embrace with a suddenness that caught him off guard.

'Is it madness, my Vicky?' he asked hoarsely, the expression in his eyes frightening her.

'Yes, it is!' she cried, a sob in her voice. 'It's madness to think one could deceive others in this way, and—and——'

Conrad advanced towards her and, without finishing her sentence, Vicky fled to where she had tethered her horse and, spurring it on to a terrific pace, she headed for the homestead without looking back. The wind whistled past her ears and stung her cheeks. She was unaware of the magnificent sight she presented with her hair streaming out behind her, her slender body arched and moving rhythmically with the mount beneath her. She was conscious only of a dull ache in her heart which she could not, and would not explain.

CHAPTER EIGHT

ANTON and Elinor de Jongh arrived the following week and they made it embarrassingly obvious that they approved of Conrad's choice of a wife. All at once Vicky hated herself and Conrad for deceiving these two wonderful people, and she made a firm decision to discuss this matter with Conrad as soon as they had a moment alone.

Anton de Jongh, despite the fact that his hair was almost white, had a remarkably good physique for his age. Conrad resembled his father in every way, Vicky noticed, even to the humorous, teasing glint in the steel-grey eyes. Elinor de Jongh looked small and petite beside her husband, with a figure that had lost none of its slenderness and grace. Her fair hair had gone silvery with age and, surprisingly, she was the same height as Vicky. Vicky recalled then what Conrad had told her about the de Jongh men all being big, and their wives small. This, she told herself hastily, was in no way applicable to herself and her own smallness.

'I must admit that when Conrad telephoned us to say that he was to be married, it came as quite a shock,' Elinor remarked one morning while they were having tea alone on the stoep. 'We would have preferred it to be a church wedding, but then Conrad obviously had other ideas. No matter how brief the ceremony was, I'm happy that we managed to be there with you.'

Vicky lowered her glance guiltily. 'I'm sorry.'

'Oh, please, Vicky,' Elinor said hastily, a warm smile on her delicate features. 'I should know my son by now. When he decides on something, he acts instantly, and it would have amazed us even more if he had indulged in a lengthy courtship before eventually marrying. Conrad has never been the patient kind.'

Vicky did not comment on this and merely drank her tea in silence. Caesar and Cleo were sprawled on the steps, basking in the sun and snapping occasionally at a persistent fly. She smiled to herself as she watched those two lovable brutes who had become her constant companions.

'Conrad told us that your brother, Michael, was so terribly keen on farming,' Elinor continued as she helped herself to more tea. 'That's why he thought it such a good idea for Michael to come here with you so that he could gain some practical experience.'

'Oh?' Vicky looked startled.

Elinor glanced at her keenly. 'You seem surprised?'

Vicky gathered her wits about her quickly. 'I am surprised that Conrad told you this, and that you obviously don't seem to mind?'

'Why should we mind, for goodness' sake?' Elinor laughed at her. 'Besides, Conrad can do with some help on the farm. He works very hard.'

'Yes. Yes, he does,' Vicky acknowledged, for despite Michael's earlier allegations that Conrad sat back and made him do all the dirty work, Vicky knew this was not so. Conrad was not one to shirk his duties, no matter what those duties entailed.

'I'm very glad Conrad married you, Vicky,' Elinor said, interrupting Vicky's thoughts and causing her to glance sharply at the woman reclining in a chair opposite her. 'You're happy here at Duiwelspoort?'

Vicky swallowed at the constriction in her throat. 'Yes. Yes, I'm very happy here.'

This was at least the truth. However strange her own words sounded to her ears, she was happy here on this Karroo farm, and when the time came for her to leave, it would not be without a certain amount of sadness at having

138

to leave behind the things which had become so much a part of her life.

'Conrad can be rather a difficult person to get on with,' Elinor continued happily. 'You must love him very much?'

'I——' Vicky's glance was startled, her cheeks stained pink. 'Yes, I do—love him.' It had been easy uttering these words of assurance to Michael and Rodney, but Elinor de Jongh was a different matter. It made the lie something loathsome; the sin even greater.

Elinor laughed unsuspectingly. 'You remind me very much of myself. It took me two years to speak of my love for Anton without blushing.'

Vicky smiled nervously and was thankful to see Conrad striding up the driveway towards them, his hat at the usual rakish angle, his boots dusty. The dogs ran to meet him, jumping up against him boisterously until he gave a sharp command that simmered them down. Tanned and virile, and smelling of the sun, he mounted the steps in one long stride and stopped in front of Vicky, his glance taking in her pink cheeks. He took hold of her hands and pulled her out of her chair.

'Has my mother been saying things to make you blush?' he asked, running a finger along her cheek.

'I asked her if she loved you,' Elinor admitted laughingly, her eyes adoringly on Conrad and Vicky.

'And do you?'

His glance was tender and teasing as he slipped an arm about her waist and held her to him, but Vicky sensed the urgency in that question, and the deception continued.

'You—know I do.'

Conrad lowered his head and, to his mother's delight, kissed Vicky long and lingeringly on the lips, and despite herself, Vicky was unable to stem the rise of colour in her cheeks.

Elinor was satisfied, Vicky could tell. They had played

their parts convincingly, but the achievement merely increased the tight little ache in Vicky's throat.

That evening when they were alone together in Vicky's room, she decided to speak to Conrad about their deceptive actions.

'It's wrong, Conrad,' she pleaded. 'Do you realise what it will do to them when they find out?'

'They can know the truth when the year is up,' he insisted, and no amount of arguing would make him desist from this decision.

His hands rested on her shoulders for a moment, then slid down the length of her arms to take her hands in his. Relentlessly he drew her closer to him until she was pressed against his tall muscular frame, his warm male fragrance weakening her resistance.

'Don't let it worry you, Vicky,' he said softly, lowering his head and kissing her satisfyingly. Against her will he drew a response from her that never failed to surprise her, and her submission always seemed to rouse him to a passion that frightened her with its intensity.

'We don't have to indulge in play-acting when we're alone,' she reprimanded him weakly when she eventually managed to tear her lips from his.

'But practice makes perfect.' He grinned and his caressing hands burned her skin through the thin material of her dress. His lips sought the hollow in her throat and the soft warmth of her shoulder, and Vicky felt faint with an uncommon desire pulsing through her veins. She could feel his thudding heartbeats beneath her fingertips as she tried to push him away.

'No!' she gasped. 'Conrad, please leave me alone!'

Never had she dreamed she could have so little resistance against a man. Conrad had a way of sweeping aside all coherent thought until she was pliable clay in his hands. She had to fight against this overpowering feeling, she realised, but her body ignored the urgent messages being flashed from her brain.

Conrad laughed at her apparent weakness and lowered his head. If he kissed her again she would be lost, she feared, and quickly she placed her hand between his lips and hers.

'Please, Conrad, this must stop,' she pleaded tremulously.

The ardour in his eyes died down and he released her instantly. 'Why are you so afraid of love, Vicky?'

His question shook her and she turned away from him, walking towards the window to stare out into the night. 'I'm not afraid of love, but this is not love, it's ...'

'Desire?' he filled in quickly, coming up behind her and turning her to face him. 'For a woman of twenty-six you appear to be remarkably innocent. It's time you grew up, Vicky, and faced the truth. Goodnight.'

Alone at last, Vicky undressed slowly and slid between the cool sheets, snapping off the light as she did so. What had Conrad implied? she wondered frowningly. Was she so innocent? And, what was the truth she had to face? She settled back against the pillows and allowed her eyes to roam about the room. The moonlight filtered in through the window, making every object visible to her and as if seeking the truth from their solidity, she let her eyes linger on their familiarity.

Sleep would evade her that night, she knew, for her thoughts were incoherent, her nerves jumpy. Nothing made sense any more, everything that was said appeared to have a hidden meaning which evaded her constantly and left her more frustrated than before. Least of all could she understand herself, and her own devastating emotions.

Vicky turned over and closed her eyes. In the next room she could hear Conrad moving about and this unsettled her more. What was he thinking? Was he hating this senseless marriage of theirs as much as she did? Since the arrival of his parents, his shaving soap and razor had been left on the shelf in her bathroom. On the dressing-table were his brush and comb, the inevitable pipe, and quite often his clothes were draped across the chair.

'We have to make it look realistic,' he had said one evening when, dressed for bed, he had wandered into her bedroom to place his clothes there. The heavy boots he wore each day were dropped unceremoniously at the foot of the bed and Vicky had stared at him with wide-eyed amusement. It all bordered on the ridiculous, and yet there was something about his clothes scattered about her room that caught at her throat and stirred something within her breast.

Vicky pummelled her pillow and turned over once more. Why were her thoughts in such a turmoil? Why could life not have continued in the comfortable way she had been accustomed to?

Natalie surprised Vicky by becoming a constant visitor at the homestead during Anton and Elinor's visit. There was no doubt that they were fond of her, and she of them.

'She grew up before our very eyes,' Elinor explained one day. 'Natalie is a truly delightful child.'

Vicky did not contradict this statement, but in her heart she felt that Natalie was no longer a child, but a woman. A woman who was beautiful, and who appeared to know exactly what she wanted from life. And Conrad, Vicky was certain, was one of the things Natalie wanted. She usually had very little to say to Vicky, but whenever Conrad appeared she seemed to come alive, capturing his attention and holding it for the duration of her visit. If their actions at times aroused Anton and Elinor's suspicions, Conrad cleverly dispelled them by an overpowering and embarrassing display of affection towards Vicky that never failed to amuse and delight his parents.

It was then that Vicky almost hated him. He was taking

unfair advantage of the situation, knowing that she could not ward off his advances in front of them.

On several occasions Vicky accompanied Conrad's parents on a visit to Otto and Sonia van Buuren. They were old friends, having been neighbours for so many years, and Vicky could understand why, for Otto and Sonia were delightful people.

As Christmas approached, the activity on the farm seemed to increase. The farm labourers were driven to town on the lorries to do their Christmas shopping, their emotions heightened by the festive season and making them burst into song at the slightest provocation. Lizzie, too, walked about singing most of the time, her songs quaint and true to her race.

The preparations for the Christmas dinner began in earnest and both Elinor and Vicky invaded the kitchen, to Lizzie's delight, to help with the baking of the Christmas pudding and the planning of the meal.

'It's always so hot on Christmas Day,' Elinor complained, 'but I somehow can't visualise the dinner without the roast turkey and plum pudding.'

Vicky agreed happily. It was many years since she had enjoyed a Christmas dinner with all the usual trimmings, she realised. Her mother's failing health had made this impossible, and they had usually ended up with cold meats and salads for dinner.

On Christmas Eve Conrad called Vicky into his study. 'I have a present for you and I thought it better to give it to you now. It will save you the embarrassment of having to thank me in front of my parents.'

Vicky stared at the small parcel he extended towards her. 'What is it?' she asked foolishly.

'Open it and see.'

With some reluctance she tugged at the ribbon and unfolded the paper. A small box fell into her hand and an

143

uncomfortable little pulse throbbed in her throat. The lid flew open as she pressed the catch and her breath caught sharply in her throat. Against the dark blue velvet nestled the most glittering diamond ring Vicky had ever seen. On either side of the large stone there were three small blue sapphires to set it off to perfection.

'It's a rather belated engagement ring,' Conrad explained.

'I—I can't accept this,' she stammered. 'It's—you shouldn't have done this.'

'Was there anything in our agreement that said I couldn't buy my wife a gift if I wanted to?'

Vicky bit her trembling lip to steady it. 'I don't deserve this, Conrad.'

He heaved an exasperated sigh and removed the small box from her unresisting fingers. He lifted the ring from its velvety cushion and caught hold of her hand, slipping the ring on to her finger. 'Now you have an engagement ring as well as a wedding ring. If you don't like it we can always exchange it.'

'I think it's beautiful,' she said quickly, staring down at her hand. 'I don't know what to say.'

'Thank you, will do very nicely,' he said drily, and Vicky, touched beyond measure, did far more than that. She reached up, drawing his head down, and kissed him lightly on the lips.

'Thank you, Conrad,' she whispered, suddenly self-conscious. It was the first time she had kissed him of her own volition and the silence that followed was tense.

'It appears as though I should buy you gifts more often,' Conrad remarked, his voice deep and vibrating with some inner emotion Vicky could not fathom. 'It's the first time you've kissed me of your own free will, and although it lacked the usual passion, you're improving.'

'Don't tease me.' Her cheeks grew hot under his intense scrutiny.

'Come,' he said at length, 'let's join the parents in the living-room.'

Elinor was ecstatic about Vicky's gift from Conrad and to her it represented a gesture of his undying love for Vicky. Elinor was a romantic at heart, Vicky realised, and it would have shocked her tremendously to have discovered the truth. Vicky hated the idea of having to shatter her dreams one day, for it would be almost like slapping an innocent baby.

After dinner that evening they exchanged gifts and Conrad was obviously delighted with Vicky's gift. It was a stinkwood pipe-rack, delicately carved and made to accommodate six pipes.

With a finger beneath her chin he tilted her head and kissed her lightly on the lips. 'How astute of you to notice that I needed something like this.'

'I couldn't help noticing that you left your pipes lying all over the house,' she replied calmly. 'This is by way of a gentle hint that you should keep them together in one place.'

Anton, also a pipe-smoker, laughed heartily. 'Vicky, it appears that my son has had the misfortune to marry the same kind of woman as I have. Elinor has spent our entire married life dropping gentle hints about my untidiness, and what has she gained by it?'

'Nothing, except being accused of nagging,' Elinor chimed in, passing a loving hand over his white hair.

Anton nodded and smiled at Vicky. 'Wait until you've been married for about a year, and see if Conrad doesn't accuse you of nagging.'

Wait until they had been married a year! A year! That was how long their marriage would last. Twelve months, of which seven had already passed. Would she, after it was all over, be able to settle down into her old routine? The daily routine at the office and the quiet evenings at home suddenly presented a distasteful picture, and Vicky hastily pushed her thoughts aside.

Anton and Elinor were returning to their home at George shortly before New Year and it was decided to have the van Buuren family over to dinner on the eve of their departure. Vicky was not looking forward to this dinner party, for the strain of having to make her relationship with Conrad appear natural was beginning to tell on her. She was nervous and jumpy, her anger erupting at the slightest provocation. Michael, too, was quick to notice this change in her.

'What's troubling you, Vicky?' he asked one morning when she joined him for breakfast in the kitchen. 'Your in-laws can't be getting on your nerves, they're such nice people. You're not ill, are you?'

'No, I'm not ill,' she replied, shaking her head, 'and my in-laws are not getting on my nerves. It's just ...' What could she say? How could she explain the tension that was building up inside her like a tightly coiled spring? 'Perhaps it's the weather,' she ended lamely. 'There's a storm brewing and the heat is oppressive. I'll feel better when it's rained.'

Michael did not seem altogether sure whether he should believe her, but he knew better than to probe further.

The evening of the dinner party arrived, and Vicky was thankful that Rodney was able to come as well. His presence would at least relieve some of her tension and nervousness. Michael appeared to be moody but not entirely unsociable and Vicky noticed that on several occasions Natalie endeavoured to strike up a conversation with him, but she gave up eventually, devoting her attention entirely to Conrad for the rest of the evening.

The dinner was a tremendous success, thanks to Lizzie's expertise in the kitchen, and when they eventually retired to the living-room to have their coffee, the atmosphere was relaxed and pleasant. Conrad's parents and the van Buurens

146

obviously found great delight in each other's company, for they talked incessantly. Vicky was glad of this, for it meant that no particular attention would be paid to her, personally, or to how she behaved towards her husband.

'May I say that you look extremely attractive this evening?' Rodney remarked, seating himself beside her. His glance swept over her, taking in her pale blue chiffon dress with the halter neck which displayed tanned smooth shoulders. 'You do, you know,' he insisted, noticing the disbelief in her golden-brown eyes.

'You're very kind.'

'Nonsense! I always speak the truth, you know that.'

Vicky lowered her glance, remembering the time he had confessed to loving her. He could have remained silent, pretending his interest was that of a casual friend, but he had not. He had told her the truth. He loved her and he did not wish to hide the fact. Yes, Rodney always spoke the truth, she had to admit to herself, and for a moment she allowed his compliment to give her the false security she needed.

Vicky glanced across the room to where Conrad and Natalie stood deep in conversation, and she felt a tug of envy at seeing them together like that. If only her own relationship with him could have been as uncomplicated, as natural, instead of the barriers of restraint they continually erected as a defence in each other's company.

Michael stood about restlessly and Vicky called him over to join herself and Rodney. He seemed reluctant, but came nevertheless. Rodney drew him into conversation, asking him how he was adapting to life on a farm, and Vicky sat back with amazement and watched the glow on Michael's face as he spoke to Rodney enthusiastically. Since the day he and Conrad had sorted things out, the change in Michael had been remarkable. It was almost as if he had been given a new lease of life, she mused to herself.

Vicky glanced about the room. Conrad and Natalie were

147

nowhere to be seen and she wondered abstractedly where they could be. With all the doors and windows open the air was still hot and stuffy in the house, and the headache she had nursed all afternoon seemed to increase to a steady throb. Where were Conrad and Natalie? What were they doing?

She excused herself and left the living-room as unobtrusively as possible. Outside on the stoep the air was refreshingly cool and Vicky leaned against the rail and closed her eyes. The night was still and peaceful, with the sweet smell of gardenias permeating the air.

Her eyes flew open at the sound of voices coming from the garden. Could it be they? She glanced searchingly in the direction of the sound and there, in the shadows of the trees, she caught sight of Natalie, her white dress shimmering in the dark. She was not alone; Vicky recognised Conrad's tall, familiar figure beside her in the darkness. They were standing close together and Natalie's head was bent, almost as though she was resting it against Conrad's broad chest, and his arms were about her.

Vicky stepped back from the rail swiftly as though she had been slapped, and allowed the darkness to enfold her. She sucked her breath in sharply through her clenched teeth as an agonising pain shot through her. She closed her eyes momentarily as the world seemed to tilt crazily about her, her mind reeling. Only one thought raced frantically through her brain; she had to get away before they saw her ... but her legs refused to co-operate, and she leaned back against the wall as jealousy, strong and vibrant, surged through her.

It was then that the explanation for her own reaction came to her with appalling clarity, sending tremor after tremor through her body. All these months she had been fighting against the unfathomable emotions churning within her, but now she understood. She cared! She loved! This

148

was why she had been unable to resist him; why a look, a touch, had sent her pulse rate soaring rapidly, and the knowledge was more painful than she had ever dreamed it would be. To love should be a joy, not this desperate, aching longing and need while knowing it was futile. Oh, why had she not realised it before? she asked herself admonishingly. Why had she been such a fool as to give her heart where it was not wanted?

Tears of rage and self-pity filled her eyes and rolled down her cheeks as, for a few brief moments, she allowed herself to wallow in the luxury of it. Tears would not help her now, she realised eventually. Conrad had married her for reasons known only to himself ... perhaps for his own amusement, but during the remainder of her stay she would have to fight against her own emotions. If she wished to lead a normal life once more, she would have to banish this newly discovered love from her heart. One thing she was determined not to do, and that was to let him see how much he had hurt her. The moment his parents left, she would see to it that their relationship became as cool and impersonal as it had been before the arrival of Anton and Elinor de Jongh.

Vicky hurried upstairs to her bedroom to remove the traces of her recent tears. Conrad's Christmas present glittered on her finger, and the mockery of it sent a searing pain through her as she applied herself to the repairs to her make-up. It would not do to have people finding clues in her appearance, she decided as, pale but composed, she returned to their guests a few minutes later.

Conrad and Natalie entered the living-room shortly after Vicky. While Conrad's expression gave nothing away, Vicky could have sworn that Natalie's eyes appeared unnaturally bright, almost as if she had recently ... shed tears? Determined not to give way to her own emotions, Vicky responded to Rodney's entertaining conversation with an enthusiasm that filled him with delight. On several occasions she caught Conrad's frowning glance, but this only encouraged her to behave even more daringly.

She glanced intently at Rodney for a moment and what she saw in his eyes shocked her to her senses. She was actually flirting with him! Flirting in a way she had never dreamed she ever could flirt with anyone, and across the room her husband's tight-lipped expression tore at her wounded heart.

'Vicky, you're behaving strangely tonight,' Rodney said softly, his eyes searching her soul. 'I must admit that while I find it flattering to my ego, I also happen to know that this is quite unlike you. Has something happened to upset you?'

Vicky veiled her eyes instantly. 'Why does there have to be a reason for my being nice to you?'

Rodney laughed shortly. 'You've always been nice to me, my dear, but tonight you're flirting with me, and that's quite out of character. It's also earning me some very severe glances from your husband, and I can't exactly blame him.'

'I'm sorry, Rodney,' she said contritely. 'Forgive me.'

'There is nothing to forgive, Vicky,' he smiled at her, and she was grateful for his understanding.

The evening seemed endless and Vicky was utterly exhausted by the time their guests prepared to leave. Natalie walked close to Michael as they stepped out on to the stoep and, to Vicky's utter confusion, she saw Natalie slip her hand into Michael's for a brief moment. It was a gesture that was so completely confounding that Vicky found it difficult to interpret. There was no time to ponder about this as they said goodnight and watched the car drive away.

Anton and Elinor immediately retired to bed, while Vicky remained behind to clear away the empty cups and dirty ashtrays. Conrad, too, went upstairs and Vicky was relieved at not having to confront him at that late hour, but she realised he would have something to say to her once his parents had left for George.

Vicky turned out the lights and went up to her room. She undressed swiftly and slipped on her négligé before applying cleansing cream to her face to remove her make-up. What was Conrad doing? she wondered as she wiped away the last of the cream. She could hear him moving about in the next room and suddenly she was conscious of a searing longing which no amount of positive thinking would disperse. She pulled the pins from her hair, letting it fall to her shoulders, and began brushing it with long, swift strokes until it shone like pure gold.

She froze suddenly with the brush suspended above her head, for in the communicating door stood Conrad, his hands thrust into the pockets of his blue silk dressing-gown. Their glances met in the mirror and Vicky lowered the brush as he approached, embarrassingly aware of the fact that her négligé was altogether too revealing.

He stood behind her, his hands caressing her shoulders. 'You looked very lovely tonight,' he said quietly, and the eyes that met hers in the mirror sent her pulse rate into a frenzy. 'But no doubt Rodney has told you this already,' he continued, a hint of sarcasm in his voice.

Vicky's anger mounted. What kind of a fool did he think she was? His hands moved restlessly in her hair as she fought against the emotions she had sworn to suppress.

'Did you want to see me about something, Conrad?' she asked with a calmness that belied the turmoil within her.

Conrad moved round to her side and removed the brush from her fingers before pulling her to her feet. She was standing close to him, conscious of the heat of his body and, nervously, she tried to move away. Instantly his grip tightened.

'Did you have to flirt with Rodney all evening?'

'I did not flirt with Rodney,' she argued feebly, lifting her chin defiantly. 'Besides, what I do is no concern of yours.'

His hands tightened on her shoulders. 'What you do does concern me. You are my wife.'

He seemed to stress the word 'wife' and subconsciously Vicky became aware of a warning light flashing through her brain, yet despite this she ignored all danger signals as her anger rose swiftly.

'You're the one who stipulated marriage as a condition for the loan, not I!' she snapped at him. 'You may have acquired me at a price, but I'm still a free agent and I shall do as I please.'

A sharp cry escaped her lips as his fingers bit into the soft flesh of her shoulders. She stared up into his face and saw the flames of anger leaping in his eyes. His lips were drawn back tightly against his teeth, while a pulse worked frantically in his cheek.

'Don't try me too far, Vicky,' he warned, shaking her violently. 'All evening I had to sit and watch you smiling and laughing with Rodney. With him you generate a warmth and friendliness I've never seen, but the moment I come near you, you freeze.'

'Conrad, please! I'm tired, I have a headache and, frankly, this discussion is beginning to bore me.'

Conrad's body vibrated with anger as his arms closed about her like bands of steel. She loved him desperately, but he frightened her at that moment, and the pleasurable pain of his arms did nothing to alleviate the ache in her heart.

'Perhaps this will relieve your boredom,' he hissed through his teeth, and it took Vicky only a few brief seconds to guess his intentions.

She fought against him, but he merely laughed at her puny efforts, and his laughter seared through her heart and made a mockery of her love. His mouth bruised hers in a kiss that was sensual enough to drive all thought of escape from her mind, while the touch of his hands made her want to weep as she swayed against him.

She struggled feebly as he lifted her in his arms and carried her across to the bed, placing her among the pillows and at the same time stretching out an arm, flooding the room in darkness.

'Conrad, for God's sake don't do anything you might regret!' she pleaded desperately as his lips raked her neck and shoulder and deliberately explored lower, his hands pushing aside her flimsy négligé.

'I shall not regret taking what is rightfully mine,' he said harshly before silencing her effectively with his lips on hers, and Vicky endured the violence of his passion while in her heart she wept. It could have been so different, if only he had loved her too.

Long after Conrad had gone, Vicky lay awake, staring dry-eyed into the darkness. She had never thought Conrad capable of breaking his word, and yet she had only herself to blame. She had goaded him beyond endurance, and her cheeks were hot with shame as she recalled how he had forced a response from her, however unwilling. He had been a masterful lover, except for the touch of cruelty he had displayed, a cruelty which had been born of anger and resentment.

She glanced at the pillow beside her where his dark head had lain, and hated him. Yes, at that moment she hated him as passionately as she loved him! In one fell swoop he had shattered her dreams, her hopes, and her happy thoughts of all that loving entailed, for not once had he spoken the words she had longed to hear . . . that he loved her!

CHAPTER NINE

WHEN Vicky awoke the following morning Conrad was not in his room, and he did not put in an appearance until it was almost time for his parents to leave. Vicky carefully avoided his quick glance in her direction as they accompanied Anton and Elinor to the car.

'It was wonderful getting to know you, my dear,' Elinor said warmly, embracing Vicky. 'Perhaps you will persuade Conrad to visit us more often in future.'

Vicky murmured something appropriate, aware of the slightly twisted smile on Conrad's lips and the hint of anxiety in his eyes.

Anton placed a heavy arm about her shoulders. 'Don't nag my son too much,' he whispered jokingly, planting a kiss on her forehead.

Vicky smiled up into the face so much like Conrad's and swallowed at the lump in her throat.

'Have a pleasant trip,' she replied, stepping back from the car.

Conrad stood beside Vicky and Michael with a tight smile on his face until the car disappeared through the stone archway, then he turned to her.

'I must speak to you, Vicky.' He glanced meaningfully at Michael. 'Alone.'

Michael turned away with a shrug, but Vicky caught at his arm. 'Don't go!' She lifted her chin defiantly, meeting Conrad's glance unwaveringly. 'Whatever you have to say can be said in front of Michael, or not at all.'

There was a tightness about Conrad's mouth. She had the uneasy feeling that she was allowing something important to slip by, but she was determined not to weaken her resolve. Conrad seemed about to say something, then he changed his mind and, turning on his heel, he strode off to where Jim was herding the ewes into a fresh camp.

'Was that wise?' Michael wanted to know, shaking off her restraining hand. 'He's in a filthy mood today, and your refusal to speak to him could only make matters worse.'

His gentle rebuke stung, but she remained adamant. 'I know what he wanted to talk to me about, and I had no wish to discuss the subject with him.'

'Have the two of you had a disagreement?'

'I suppose you could call it that,' she replied reluctantly, struggling to ban the memory of what had happened from her mind.

'Look, Vicky,' Michael continued with an exasperated sigh, 'if I can help you in any way, will you say so?'

Her eyes grew moist. 'There's nothing you can do to help, but thank you for offering, Michael.'

He walked beside her in silence for some moments and then turned to her once more. 'I'm going to town this afternoon to collect a few things for Conrad. Want to come?'

'No,' she shook her head, 'but I would be grateful if you would post a letter for me.'

'I'll do that,' he nodded. 'Have it ready at lunchtime. I'm leaving immediately afterwards.'

Vicky stood for a moment and watched him walk away before she turned and hurried inside. For want of anything better to do she washed her hair, dried it vigorously with a towel, then merely brushed it and tied it back with a ribbon. She changed quickly into slacks and a blouse and set off in the direction of the stables.

Teresa, at least, was glad to see her and she whinnied softly, nuzzling her nose into Vicky's hand. Vicky stroked the velvety neck and murmured soothingly as Teresa quivered with suppressed energy. There was no longer any need for someone to help her saddle her mount, and Vicky went about her task with joyous anticipation. Teresa, at that moment, offered freedom, relaxation, and forgetfulness. She would not have to think, merely feel and enjoy, and that was what she needed most—not having to think . . . and remember . . . only to forget! Forget the memory of bruising arms and lips that spoke only of passion and desire, and never once of love and tenderness!

Vicky returned to the homestead an hour before lunch, feeling exhilarated and refreshed. She hastened up to her room to collect the letter she had written to Hilary some days ago and went in search of an envelope. Perhaps Conrad would have some in his study, she thought, after discovering that she had none.

The door to the study was standing ajar when she reached it, so she pushed it open further and went in. There were no envelopes on his desk, she noticed, and she decided to search through the drawers.

She pulled open the top right-hand side drawer and instantly froze with horror. Lying on top of all the other papers was a photograph of herself, standing on the beach with her hair loosened from its confining coil and swinging back from her face. She was standing with her legs slightly apart, bracing herself against the wind as it whipped her thin cotton frock against her body, revealing all too clearly the delicate curve of firm, young breasts, the slender waist, and shapely thighs. Her head was thrown back and she was laughing, her stance unconsciously seductive.

Vicky hesitantly removed the photograph from the drawer and stood staring at it for endless moments. She remembered only too well when it had been taken. She had been invited by Sam and Hilary on a picnic to a secluded little beach along the coast. The weather had been dreadful, but their spirits had been high, for Vicky was celebrating her coming of age, while Hilary was rejoicing at the discovery that she was expecting her first child. Vicky had returned from a walk along the beach, struggling against the wind, and Sam, camera handy, had taken that photograph despite the fact that she had protested laughingly.

Where, and how, had Conrad managed to get this copy? Her mind raced madly, dwelling on every possibility. Sam had given her the only available print and, shocked by what she had seen, she had destroyed it, begging Sam to do the same with the negative. It was obvious now that he had not done so, and that Conrad had somehow acquired this print from Sam. But why? How? And for what purpose?

Had he sometimes sat and stared at it during those long hours he had spent alone in his study? And what had his thoughts been on those occasions? she wondered frantically. Had he perhaps come to the conclusion that she had struck a deliberately seductive pose? That she was *that* sort of person; someone without morals? Her family and close friends would naturally know that this was not so, and would see it as an excellent piece of photography, which it undoubtedly was. Had Conrad also seen it purely in that light? Or had he thought what any stranger might think; that her pose had been deliberately alluring?

Vicky shuddered at the thought, the blood rushing to her face, burning her eyelids and pounding at her temples, only to recede a moment later, leaving her deathly pale. She let the photograph drop back into the drawer, and at the sound of a step behind her, she swung round guiltily. Conrad's glance went from her stricken face to the open drawer, his eyes glinting like bits of steel in his pale face.

'I trust you found what you were looking for?' His voice was quietly ominous, like the distant roll of thunder threatening to erupt into the most violent storm.

'I—I was looking for an envelope.'

'Did you find one?'

'N-no.'

His eyes held hers captive. 'Instead, you found the photograph?'

'Yes.' Her reply was barely a whisper forced past unresponsive lips.

He advanced upon her with such fury that she fell back a pace, thinking he would strike her, but he stopped beside the open drawer and removed the object of her embarrassment from it. He stared long and hard at her image on paper before lifting his head to let his glance rove slowly and insultingly over her trembling form.

'It does at least give a true reflection of your character,' he snapped, flinging the photograph into the drawer and slamming it shut.

If he had struck her physically he could not have inflicted a more severe pain than the one searing through her at that moment. She cowered back against the bookshelf and wished that the floorboards would collapse beneath her weight to bury her beneath the debris, but the shelves dug into her back, forcing her to face the reality of the accusation behind his harshly spoken words. He had, after all, interpreted the photograph in the way she had feared he would.

Humiliation swept over her, leaving her weak and helpless. She clutched at the back of the swivel chair for support, but it swung away beneath her touch so that she landed in it in a crumpled heap. Too tired to care, she remained where she was, not daring to look up at him as he towered above her. She could not bear to see that look of derision in his eyes a moment longer.

'Did Sam give it to you?' she asked dully.

'Where and how I got it is my business entirely.'

'Please destroy it.'

'Why?' he demanded bluntly. 'Why hide your true character behind that cool exterior you always present to me?'

'Please!' she begged, beaten and numb with pain. 'It should have been destroyed in the first place.'

'You may destroy it if you wish,' he said bitterly, 'but I might as well tell you that I also have the negative and at any time I can have another copy made.'

Her head shot up then, her eyes wounded and angry, her face deathly white. 'I think you're despicable!'

Conrad, too, was several shades paler. 'Vicky, about last night——'

'No!' she interrupted fiercely, placing her hands over her ears. 'I don't wish to discuss last night ... now or ever!'

The next instant she was gripped violently by the arms and lifted bodily out of the chair so that she landed with a thud against his hard chest. His eyes were gleaming with rage and for one terrifying moment she thought he was going to strangle her as his hand closed about her throat, but he merely forced her face upwards, while with his other hand he pinned her hands behind her back, rendering her helpless.

'You hate me, don't you?' he demanded through his teeth, and Vicky was never quite sure whether she had imagined that look of pain in his eyes, she knew only that she wanted to lash out to inflict as much hurt as she was suffering.

'Yes, yes! I hate you!' she cried, yet in the innermost recesses of her heart she knew that she would love this cruel, hateful man for as long as there was breath in her body. He had ripped her heart from within her, taking possession of it even without her knowledge, and he had trampled it underfoot. It was no longer hers to redeem, but his to do with as he pleased.

Conrad's mouth came down hard on hers and bruised

her already tender lips as he forced them apart. His kisses became deliberately sensual and, despite her rigid control, he drew yet again a response from her that left her limp and trembling in his arms as she returned his kiss with a passion that made her light-headed, with a complete disregard of the consequences.

He released his grip on her arms, sliding his hands possessively over her hips while his lips sought the softness of her shoulder. Vicky's hands crept up the front of his rough safari jacket. The top button had come undone and her fingers felt the dark hair on his chest. His skin was warm beneath her touch, while his heart pounded against her through the thin material of her blouse.

Vicky despised herself as she succumbed to his caresses. Nothing mattered any more except this wild, pulsating emotion that swept through her. Then, quite unexpectedly, he released her. Vicky swayed at the suddenness of it and gripped the desk beside her. Turning on his heel, he strode from the study and slammed the door behind him.

Vicky stared at the door for a moment with a look of utter surprise on her face and then, as wave after wave of humiliation swept over her, she sank down to the floor beside the chair and wept bitter tears of self-recrimination. For the first time in many years the floodgates had been opened, and Vicky wept unrestrainedly until she was drained of all emotion.

Never would she give Conrad the opportunity again of humiliating her in this way. Never!

Life assumed a semblance of normality after that unfortunate episode. Vicky returned Conrad's personal things to his own room, and her fears that he would once again come to her, as he had that night, were unfounded. The cool, polite front they put up in each other's company lulled even Michael into believing that all was well between them. Only Vicky knew of the tension, the restraint, and the heartache she suffered daily.

Conrad seemed quite unaware of any awkwardness in Vicky, and appeared to be unmoved by the obvious shadows beneath her eyes that only lack of sleep and unhappiness could have put there. He spent more time in his study during the evenings than ever before, and quite often Michael would join him there, leaving Vicky alone and completely excluded from whatever it was they talked and laughed about. This hurt her deeply and many a night she cried herself to sleep.

The time for her departure from Duiwelspoort was approaching fast and she dreaded it far more than she had dreaded coming there. Duiwelspoort, despite everything, had become her home, and when the time came to leave, a part of her would remain forever amongst the little *kopjes* of this semi-desert country. She would miss Teresa and the wonderful rides she had had, and she would also miss Caesar and Cleo, who had been her constant companions during her stay. But most of all, she would miss Conrad, and the longing would be a painful memory to haunt her through the days and in her dreams at night.

'Madam looks sad today,' Lizzie remarked one morning while Vicky was having tea in the kitchen.

'I am sad, Lizzie,' Vicky admitted, her eyes on the distant hill where she and Conrad had stopped when she first came to Duiwelspoort. It was there that he had pointed out the boundary of the farm and had given her an idea of its vastness. 'I was thinking how unhappy I would be to leave here.'

Lizzie's dark eyes widened. 'But the Madam is not going to leave here, and Master Conrad hasn't said anything about leaving?'

A solitary tear rolled down Vicky's cheek and impatiently she dashed it away with the back of her hand. 'Don't take any notice of what I said, Lizzie. I'm just being silly.'

'Perhaps the Madam is not feeling well?' Her glance swept over Vicky. 'The Madam has got thin. Too thin!'

Vicky laughed with enforced gaiety. 'Let's stop talking about myself. Tell me about Conrad instead. What was he like as a child?'

'Naughty, Madam,' Lizzie laughed, wiping her hands on a towel and pouring Vicky another cup of tea. 'He used to tease Miss Barbara sometimes until she cried, but they were very fond of each other.'

'Did he start farming straight after he left school, or did he attend university first?'

'Master Conrad went to university first, but not to learn about farming,' Lizzie informed her promptly. 'He wanted to be a vet—vet——'

'Veterinary surgeon?' Vicky supplied quickly and with a certain amount of surprise. So this was why the neighbours occasionally asked him to take a look at their animals.

'That's right. He was at university for two years. But then there was some trouble and the *Oubaas*—that's Master Conrad's grandfather—he went straight to Stellenbosch and brought Master Conrad back with him.'

'Why? What do you mean by saying there was trouble?'

Lizzie shook her head. 'Didn't Master Conrad tell the Madam?'

'No.'

'Perhaps the Master doesn't want the Madam to know?'

'No, I think he has merely never thought about it. Tell me, Lizzie,' she egged her on.

Reluctantly Lizzie continued. 'The Master got mixed up with some characters there in Stellenbosch, and they were up to no good. Master Anton and the Madam were very worried at the time because it looked as though Master Conrad was getting to be just as bad as his friends.'

162

'What do you mean by bad? What were they doing?'

'Gambling, the *Oubaas* said. I don't know everything, Madam, just what I heard them talking about sometimes.'

Vicky stared at her aghast. 'I can't believe this! Conrad would never do such a thing!'

Lizzie nodded her head vigorously. 'He did, Madam. Master Conrad admitted that he had gambled, I heard him say so myself. The *Oubaas* said that if Master Conrad had stayed there long enough he would have allowed himself to be influenced by the others. That's why the *Oubaas* brought him back here.'

'And he came without protest? Abandoning his studies just like that?' It seemed impossible, and yet it was obviously the truth.

'Madam!' Lizzie rolled her eyes. 'When the *Oubaas* said jump, you jumped! Not even Master Conrad would go against anything his grandfather said, and Master Conrad wasn't twenty-one yet.'

'I gather he was a very strict old man.'

'Strict?' Lizzie whistled through her teeth. 'Master Conrad didn't want to farm, but the *Oubaas* drove him on with a whip like you drive cattle.'

'Surely not,' Vicky laughed in disbelief.

'Madam, I'm telling you the truth. Master Conrad learnt to farm the hard way. He had the *Oubaas* behind him all the time, and every time Master Conrad slackened off, he would feel the lash of the *Oubaas'* tongue.'

'Didn't Conrad's parents object to their son being treated in this way?'

'Of course they objected! At least, the Madam did, but Master Anton agreed with the *Oubaas*. The *Oubaas* was determined he would make a man out of Master Conrad, and he did!'

Vicky sat in silence, absorbing this fantastic information. It was as though she suddenly understood Conrad's reasons for offering to help Michael, and the way he had gone about it. He had seen a little of himself in Michael and had used his grandfather's remedy to bring about the same results. She wondered curiously if he had perhaps mentioned this to Michael that day they had had their rather violent confrontation? It would most certainly be a logical explanation for the change in Michael since that day.

This did not explain, though, why he had insisted on their marriage. Was it merely so that she could be with Michael in this way? Or had Natalie, after all, something to do with his decision? At the time she had been too anxious to help Michael to ponder about this. Conrad had insisted that she should marry him and Vicky had been too thankful for his offer of help to refuse.

To confuse her even further, Natalie started calling on her during the day, mostly for a cup of tea and a chat before she returned home. At first their conversation was stilted and filled with restraint until Vicky realised that there was no ulterior motive in the girl's visits. Natalie appeared to have grown up overnight, and Vicky discovered with amazement that she liked the girl despite the fact that she was certain of Natalie's love for Conrad.

'Mother wants to know when you are coming over to tea again,' Natalie told her one morning. 'I think she's worried about you. You're looking rather thin and peaky these days.'

Vicky evaded Natalie's searching glance. 'There's no need for your mother to be anxious about me. I'm really perfectly well.'

'One wouldn't say so, looking at you.'

Vicky smiled suddenly. 'Looks can be deceiving, Natalie. There really is nothing wrong with me, except that I'm not sleeping very well lately.'

'Shall I tell Mother you'll come along tomorrow morning?'

'Yes, do that.'

There was a late summer storm brewing, and the air was stifling. On the stoep, where Vicky usually served tea, the breeze was tepid and not at all refreshing.

'I wish it would rain,' she remarked almost to herself as she handed Natalie her tea.

'Father predicts a violent storm within the next few days,' Natalie informed her. 'He's usually right, and I'm dreading it.'

'Good heavens, why?'

'You haven't been here long enough to experience the violence of a Karroo storm.' She stirred her tea thoughtfully. 'The rivers come down in flood, fences are washed away, and the poor defenceless sheep are swept along with it. Conrad lost about eighty sheep one year when the wall of one of his dams broke under the pressure of the water. My father lost almost as many that year as well.'

'Does your father suspect we're in for one of those storms?' Vicky asked nervously.

'That's what he says.'

Natalie sat staring into the distance and quite suddenly Vicky saw her glance sharpening. Glancing unobtrusively in the same direction, Vicky saw Conrad and Michael examining the fence of one of the camps. Was it Conrad who held her attention, or Michael? Certainly not Michael, she decided firmly, ignoring the ache in her heart. The two men strolled out of sight and Natalie relaxed visibly.

'I believe Michael is to celebrate his twenty-first birthday next week,' Natalie said conversationally. 'Are you going to have a party?'

'I have thought about it, yes,' Vicky acknowledged reluctantly, 'but I haven't as yet discussed the subject with Conrad.'

'For goodness' sake, why do you first have to discuss it with him?'

Vicky stared into blue eyes that mirrored surprise. Yes,

165

she thought, why did she have to discuss it with him? If he did not wish to attend the party, he could always stay away. Could he not?

'Let's make it a surprise party,' Natalie suggested eagerly, taking matters out of Vicky's hands. 'I'll get Mother to help with the eats and we shall all arrive after dinner to wish him a happy birthday. What do you say, Vicky?'

'Well ... yes. That's a very good idea.' She made a mental note of a few things she would have to get in town, and Lizzie would be only too eager to help with the preparations. 'We'll do it!' she exclaimed, delighted at the prospect.

'Good!'

Natalie was a bundle of excitement when she left Duiwelspoort, and Vicky remained on the stoep in a puzzled frame of mind. She was finding it increasingly difficult to understand Natalie van Buuren, and the more she thought about her, the more confused she became. It was exasperating to say the least!

The storm Otto van Buuren had predicted broke loose two days later and Vicky was terrified by it. It started during the night and raged through until lunchtime the following day, leaving devastating damage in its wake. The thunder and lightning tore at Vicky's nerves and what upset her most was the fact that Conrad and Michael were out in that terrible rain checking the dam and the fences and making sure that the animals were in no danger. Her timid offer to help was turned down abruptly by Conrad, and Vicky could not decide which was worse; to be outside with the men in the terrible storm, or spending the long hours at home with only Lizzie for company as she waited? Both were equally frustrating, she decided eventually.

Conrad sent a message to the effect that they would not be home for lunch. They were repairing as much of the damage as they possibly could before nightfall. He suggested instead that Vicky send them something to eat by the

166

messenger and she lost no time in doing his bidding.

The period of waiting continued. The storm had at least abated and the sky was clearing partially, so there was no longer any fear of their being struck by lightning. Despite this consoling thought, Vicky could not shake off the premonition of disaster which invaded her thoughts. Lizzie tried to keep her occupied by giving her things to do in the kitchen, but even this could not stop her mind from wandering feverishly in circles.

It was at dusk that evening that Vicky became aware of a commotion outside. Caesar and Cleo barked and whined alternately, while Vicky remained standing quite rigidly in the centre of the kitchen.

'Something is wrong, Lizzie,' she whispered anxiously, her nails biting into the palms of her hands.

'The storm has made the Madam nervous,' Lizzie laughed.

'No! No, it's not the storm, it's——'

Conrad! Conrad has been hurt! she thought frantically, and she instantly came to life, rushing at the kitchen door and flinging it open. Before her startled eyes stood Conrad, with Michael flung across his shoulder.

'Don't panic!' he said sharply as she opened her mouth. 'He fell and he's slightly concussed. Nothing more.'

'Master Conrad?' Lizzie's face was several shades paler. 'What's wrong with Master Michael?'

'Nothing, Lizzie,' he replied with a strange abruptness. 'Nothing for you to worry about.'

'What happened?' Vicky whispered anxiously as she followed him upstairs to Michael's room.

Conrad did not reply until he had placed Michael gently on the bed. 'The gates were down and the bull charged him.'

'But it's never done anything like that before.'

'It's the storm,' Conrad explained briefly. 'The animals are all nervous and upset.'

167

'The bull didn't gore him?' Vicky searched anxiously for any sign of injury.

'I fortunately got him out of the way in time, but he caught his head a glancing blow on a wooden pole.' He regarded her intently, a strange paleness creeping up beneath the skin at the sides of his mouth. 'Do you think you could manage to get him round?'

There was no need for either of them to do that, for Michael groaned softly and opened his eyes. 'What—what——?'

'It's all right, Michael,' Vicky assured him gently, examin-the graze on the side of his head. 'You've been unconscious, but you're fine now.'

'The bull charged——'

'Yes, I know,' she said shortly. 'Lie still while I fetch the first-aid box.'

Vicky turned to leave the room and discovered that Conrad was no longer there. Where had he disappeared to so suddenly? she wondered, but there was no time to ponder over this as she hurried along to Conrad's room to collect the necessary things. She cleaned the graze on Michael's forehead and attached a piece of adhesive dressing to it.

'You're as good as new,' she told him, a smile tugging at her lips, 'except that you're very dirty.'

Michael sat up, swinging his legs off the side of the bed. 'Oh, my head!' he groaned, placing his head in his hands.

'I'll give you something for it. Here,' she dropped two tablets into his hand and held a glass of water to his lips. 'Perhaps you should lie down and rest for a while.'

He swallowed the tablets and grimaced at the taste. 'I don't think I want to lie down. I'll be fine in a minute.' He looked at her then and she almost laughed at the sight of his face streaked with mud. 'He saved my life, you know.'

'Conrad?'

He nodded and winced. 'When the bull charged he vaulted

168

the fence and threw me bodily over to the other side. That's how I knocked my head on that pole, but I could have been seriously gored if he hadn't done that.' He shook his head slightly. 'I'm amazed that the bull never got him in the end.'

Something tightened in Vicky's throat. If Conrad had been seriously injured while saving Michael's life, she would never be able to forgive herself for the terrible thoughts she had nurtured about him. It was obvious though that he had escaped unscathed, for he would not, surely, have been able to carry Michael home if he had also sustained an injury.

Michael's headache forced him back into bed after he had taken a shower and Vicky took his dinner up to him. Conrad appeared eventually, stating that he would eat later, and he promptly retired to his study. There was nothing else Vicky could do but sit down to a solitary meal which, after a few minutes, she found she was unable to eat.

Lizzie shook her head at Vicky's untouched plate and returned to the kitchen, muttering to herself. She washed the dishes and tidied the kitchen before leaving and the house became peculiarly quiet, almost as though it was holding its breath.

Natalie arrived in her father's car and Vicky was actually glad to see her.

'I only heard a short while ago about Michael's accident,' she explained. 'I thought I would call to find out how he is.'

Vicky explained what had happened. 'If you like you could go upstairs and see him for a few minutes.'

Natalie hesitated a moment. 'He won't object, will he?'

'Why should he?'

Natalie shrugged her shoulders and went upstairs, leaving Vicky alone once more.

Vicky heard Conrad walking about in his study and could not shake off her concern for him. What would he do if she went to him now? He did not seem able to tolerate her presence lately and she could quite probably collect a rebuff for her trouble, she decided, hovering outside the study door. Something clattered to the floor and she heard him swear lightly, but still she remained where she was. It was only when, seconds later, something else fell to the floor, that Vicky pursed her lips firmly and opened the door.

Conrad was standing with his hands resting on the desk, his head bent. Vicky's glance went to his side and she stood for a moment, her breath locked in her throat as she saw the stain of blood on his shirt.

'You're hurt!' she cried, horrified, unable to tear her eyes away from his side.

Conrad turned to her then with a look of anger on his face. 'Can't you leave me alone?'

Vicky came to him swiftly. 'Why didn't you tell me you were hurt? Let me have a look.'

'No!' He caught hold of her hands and held her at bay. 'It's nothing. Go to bed!'

'Conrad, don't be ridiculous. Let me help you.'

'Are you sure you could stomach it?' he asked as he met her steady glance. His lips tightened suddenly with obvious pain and he looked away. 'Go ahead, Nurse Vicky.'

She lifted his shirt and removed the soaked dressing to expose the long, ragged, gaping wound. Vicky swallowed violently, stemming the upsurge of nausea.

'For God's sake, Conrad,' she breathed. 'You need a doctor, not a strip of sticking plaster.'

'Now you're being ridiculous,' he laughed unsteadily, and promptly sagged against the desk. 'My God, I'm going to faint.'

Vicky slipped in under his arm and took the full impact of his weight upon her shoulder. Fear clamoured in her throat as she lowered him into a chair.

'Hello, what's going on here?'

Vicky glanced up quickly to see Natalie standing in the doorway. 'I knocked, but apparently no one heard.'

'Natalie, I'm so glad you're here,' Vicky cried with a certain amount of relief. 'Conrad has been hurt and I must get him to a doctor.'

'Don't fuss,' Conrad groaned weakly. 'It's just a scratch.'

Vicky bit her lip and ignored him. 'Natalie, do you think you could fetch the Holden from the garage and bring it round to the front door? The key is on the hook beside the fridge.'

It was only then that Natalie realised the urgency of the matter and her blue eyes were wide and anxious as she hurried out to do as Vicky had requested.

There was no time to renew Conrad's dressing and she could not leave him alone for fear that he would do himself a further injury.

Michael appeared in the doorway in his pyjamas and gown. 'I thought I heard the Holden. What's going on?'

'Conrad has been hurt.'

'Not the——' He held a hand to his head. 'Oh, my God! Not the bull?'

'Stop fussing,' Conrad said, gritting his teeth in agony and Vicky felt her heart twist within her breast.

'Do you think you could lean on me?' she asked Conrad gently. 'I'll help you into the Holden.'

'I'm too heavy,' he protested, but at the sound of the Holden approaching, Vicky hesitated not a second longer. She took hold of his hand and slipped under his arm once more, placing her other arm about him for added support without hurting his wound further.

'Come on, Conrad. On your feet.'

It was a near impossible task getting Conrad outside and into the Holden, but between Michael, Natalie and herself, they managed it. Although he was conscious, it appeared as though he had lost a tremendous amount of blood, for he was near to fainting most of the time. She felt as though every muscle in her body ached by the time she slid behind the wheel.

'I'll come with you,' Michael said anxiously, and still slightly groggy from the tablets she had given him.

'No, you won't!' Vicky said swiftly. 'It's bad enough having one patient on my hands. Two would be impossible.'

'But, Vicky——'

'Telephone the doctor instead, and tell him I'm on my way,' she interrupted. 'I'll need help to get Conrad out of the Holden.'

'I'll go ahead and open the gates for you,' Natalie offered, her eyes anxiously on Conrad's reclining form beside Vicky.

'Thank you, Natalie,' Vicky replied, starting the engine as Natalie ran to her own car and drove ahead.

It was impossible to pick up speed on the road to Koelenberg. In places it had been partially washed away and Vicky had to crawl through at a snail's pace. Conrad remained conscious throughout the journey, for occasionally she heard him groan softly when the Holden bumped unexpectedly. It was all in all the worst journey Vicky had ever undertaken, and it was only her fear that something would happen to Conrad that made her push on. He must not die! He must not! If anything happened to Conrad ... ! She shook herself slightly. To have to live without him was unthinkable!

The fear of losing someone precious can be an agonising experience, as Vicky was discovering, and the knowledge that he would most probably hate her afterwards, for seeing him so helpless only added to her anxieties. Conrad was a proud man. Too proud ever to accept help from anyone. But tonight he had had to accept help from her, a woman, and the blow to his male ego would have an added sting.

CHAPTER TEN

DOCTOR STEWART'S consulting room was in the grounds of his home and he was waiting outside as Vicky drove through the gates. Between the two of them they managed to get Conrad into the surgery and on to the couch. He removed the makeshift dressing and whistled through his teeth, although his features remained impassively calm.

'How did this happen?'

Vicky explained what had occurred while her heart contracted violently at the sight of Conrad's pale, still form. He was conscious and obviously in pain, for his bottom lip was caught between his teeth and the beads of perspiration stood out on his forehead.

'Is it serious?' Vicky whispered anxiously as the elderly doctor completed his examination.

He shook his head. 'The cut is not as deep as it appears, and fortunately there are no further injuries. I'll clean and stitch the wound and give him a shot of penicillin.' He moved away to wash his hands and collect his instruments. 'If you wish, Mrs de Jongh, you may wait in the next room.'

Vicky glanced swiftly at Conrad. She did not want to leave him, but perhaps he would prefer it. His hand moved then and caught at hers.

'Stay—if you can face it,' he muttered, and for some inexplicable reason Vicky felt an upsurge of tenderness and exquisite joy.

Her lips curved delicately into a smile. 'I'll stay if that's what you want.'

He nodded his dark head and the warm pressure of his hand increased as he regarded her steadily with the most unfathomable expression in his grey eyes.

Standing there beside Conrad, holding his hand tightly while the doctor stitched his wound, was an experience Vicky thought she would never forget as long as she lived. At times her teeth were clamped so tightly together that her throat ached. She had to appear unconcerned for Conrad's sake, for his eyes never left her face for one moment, and any show of squeamishness would have brought that gleam of mockery to his eyes which she had come to hate so intensely. Her stomach nerves quivered at the sight she had to witness, and occasionally she had to swallow violently to stem her rising nausea.

When it was all over, Doctor Stewart suggested that they stay the night, but Conrad insisted that he wanted to return home. Doctor Stewart's kindly face puckered into a frown.

'Will you be able to manage, Mrs de Jongh?'

'Yes. Yes, I think so,' she replied as they helped Conrad into the Holden. 'Goodnight, Doctor Stewart, you have been most kind.'

To Vicky's relief Jim was waiting at the main gate when they arrived home. After letting her through, he closed the gate and jumped into the back of the Holden.

'When Master Michael told us what had happened, I thought I would wait for the Madam to return with the Master so that I could open the gates and perhaps help the Madam get the Master to bed,' he explained, glancing anxiously at Conrad. 'Is the Master all right?'

'I'm not dead yet, Jim.' Conrad spoke suddenly, and both Vicky and Jim glanced at him in surprise.

'I thought you were asleep,' Vicky remarked.

'How can I sleep when you jolt me about like a sack of potatoes?'

Jim's happy laughter rang out from the back seat. 'Nay, if the Master can talk like that, then the Master is going to be all right. I can see that.'

'Where is Michael?' Vicky asked anxiously.

'Master Michael went back to bed, Madam. He said that his head was still sore.' Jim laughed again. 'Master Michael will be all right, Madam. He's tough.'

At the homestead Jim helped Vicky to get Conrad upstairs. It was a devilish situation, but Vicky had no option but to take Conrad to her own bedroom. They lowered him on to the bed and Jim hovered for a moment until Vicky thanked him, informing him that she would manage further without help. Conrad was drowsy now and a peculiar little smile hovered about his lips as Vicky helped him remove his shirt. She ignored this for the moment and continued to remove his shoes and socks before covering him with a rug.

'What's so funny?' she asked sharply.

'You,' he said promptly. 'This whole business.'

Vicky glanced at him severely. 'If you have any intention of becoming hysterical, I warn you I shall slap you!'

'You must see the funny side of it too, Vicky. Here I am lying in your bed because you couldn't very well take me anywhere else with Jim around. To crown it all, you have to undress me.'

He was obviously lightheaded, she decided. 'That's not funny!'

Conrad sobered slightly at the severity in her voice, but the glint in his eyes did not disappear. 'I can't sleep with my trousers on.'

Her cheeks were burning hot. 'You'll just have to.'

Conrad did not argue. He was clearly exhausted, for no sooner had she made him comfortable than he dropped off to sleep. Vicky pulled a chair closer and sat beside him for a while. It was strange how defenceless one looked in sleep, she thought as she sat there looking at him. The harsh lines of his face had softened and he looked almost young and boyish, his stern, finely chiselled lips relaxed and curved into the semblance of a smile. Vicky leaned forward with the strong desire to brush her own lips against his, but, shocked at what she had been contemplating, she withdrew hastily and leaned back in her chair, squirming inwardly to imagine the mockery in his eyes if he had awakened at that moment.

Conrad slept soundly, his broad chest lifting and falling softly, and he was no longer so frighteningly pale. An hour went by and Vicky's head began to nod with fatigue. She moved her arms and legs stiffly and arched her back. How she had managed to take Conrad's weight on her own slight frame, she would never know, and could only imagine that she had gained strength which was born of fear. Fear for Conrad; of losing him! Even now she could recall the frightened beat of her heart at the sight of his large frame sagging against the desk with the blood staining his shirt.

If anything had happened to Conrad . . .! She instantly rejected her appalling thoughts to discover that her eyes were brimming with tears. She dashed them away quickly and rose to her feet.

'Vicky?'

She turned sharply to see Conrad moving restlessly in his sleep. She caught his hand as it groped in her direction and held it between her own. Instantly his fingers tightened about hers.

He groaned softly in his sleep. 'Vicky, please stay. Don't go—don't go.'

He clearly did not know what he was saying, she decided as she reassured him gently that she would not leave. Tomorrow, she thought as he settled down once more, tomorrow he would not remember these words he had uttered and to remind him would merely cause her, and him, embarrassment.

When she was certain that he was asleep she slipped her hand from his and snapped off the light. She walked stiffly round to the other side of the bed and gently, so as not to wake him, she eased herself on to the bed beside him. If he should need her during the night she had to be close at hand, certain that his slightest movement would wake her. After that terrifying storm it seemed strange to see the moon filtering in through the lace curtains, and Vicky lay for a moment staring at Conrad's dark head so close to her own until her heavy eyelids drooped, and she slept.

Vicky awoke with a start to find the sun streaming in through the window, the slight breeze lifting the curtains. The rug she had used to cover Conrad with was now placed carefully about her, and Conrad was no longer beside her.

'Conrad?' she called, but there was no reply, and then she realised why. Someone was moving about in the bathroom, and it could be no one other than Conrad.

She threw the rug aside and swiftly gathered a few oddments of clothing before going to the other bathroom further down the passage. She had not bothered to change the night before and her appearance was dishevelled, her slacks and blouse creased. She bathed and changed as quickly as she could, but by the time she returned to her room the bathroom was vacant and from the sound of cupboard doors being opened and closed she gathered that he was in his own room, changing.

She went swiftly to the door, then hesitated. She had never asked to be admitted to his room while he was present, and she was still hovering with indecision when the door opened and Conrad stood framed in it, his mocking glance taking in her appearance.

'You shouldn't be walking about!' Embarrassment gave a sharp edge to her voice, which she regretted instantly as his face became a mask of indifference.

'I am perfectly capable of deciding what I should or should not do,' he said coldly, his eyes pinning her to the floor. 'I would like to apologise for the inconvenience I caused you last night. Your concern for me was touching, but it's no longer necessary.'

Anger swelled in her throat and left her speechless. How typical that he should belittle her efforts when every fibre of her being had been centred upon his welfare! She had not expected him to thank her profusely, but neither had she expected this patronising attitude he had adopted. He had power to hurt her more deeply than anyone else, and he wielded that power with satanic delight, it appeared.

She choked back the tears, lifting her chin proudly. 'I have no intention of wasting concern on someone who doesn't need it. What I did for you, I would have done for anyone else in the same circumstances, and—and I'm glad that you are no longer in need of my services.'

She turned on her heel and would have left the room had he not called her back.

She turned to face him and she lost count of time as they stared at each other. Caesar and Cleo barked as they romped on the lawn, and the sound jarred against her nerves.

Conrad drew a deep breath as he walked across to the bed and sat down heavily. 'Vicky, I want to talk to you.'

A nerve jumped in her throat. 'What about?'

He gestured vaguely. 'Sit down.'

Vicky sat down reluctantly in the straight-backed stink-wood chair and noticed for the first time the lines of strain along the side of his mouth. His dark head was bent, his shoulders slightly hunched as he sat with his hands tightly clenched between his knees.

'If you want to return to Cape Town, then I shan't hold you to the agreement we made,' he said eventually, his voice grating against her already sensitive nerves. 'I won't keep you here at Duiwelspoort until the year is up.'

'Thank you very much.' Her words were clipped, the tight ache in her throat making it difficult to breathe.

178

His glance sharpened. 'What will you do when you get there?'

Vicky met his glance steadily for a moment before getting to her feet and walking across to the window to stare out at the garden where the morning sunlight glittered on the dew and gave an added brilliance to the already colourful sight.

'What I intend doing in the future does not concern you,' she replied with her back to him. She could not let him see the wild desperation in her eyes at that moment, for the mask of indifference had been momentarily lifted to reveal the agony of loving and knowing that she was not wanted.

'It does concern me,' he continued gravely. 'I would like to give you all the financial help you need to——'

'I don't want your financial help!' she cried despairingly. 'Only your love,' a little voice wailed within her heart.

'Nevertheless, you're going to get it,' he insisted quietly. 'Don't be stubborn, Vicky. Surely I have some right to know your future plans?'

Vicky's head drooped. 'I don't know what Michael intends to do eventually, but I shall return to the city and try to pick up where I left off.'

'Michael won't be returning to the city,' he told her calmly, and as she swung round to face him, he asked: 'Didn't he tell you?'

There was a stunned pause while she assimilated the shock. 'What do you mean?'

His heavy shoulders moved slightly. 'I've bought another farm adjoining my own and Michael wishes to remain permanently in order to farm it for me.'

'Oh, I see.' It was difficult to believe that Michael, who had been so dead against coming to the farm in the first place, was now willing to remain indefinitely, and of his own free will. 'Why did you marry me, Conrad?'

The silence was quite deafening. What on earth had possessed her to ask that question? She wondered. What possible difference could the reason make at that moment? It was a ridiculous question, uttered without thinking, and an open invitation for him to subject her to further mockery.

'It was one of the conditions of the loan, remember?'

'Was that all?' the words were wrung from her.

'No, damn you, that was not all!' he said savagely, getting to his feet and advancing towards her in two long strides. His violent actions made him wince while Vicky remained where she was, unable to move even if she had wanted to. His features, as he glared down at her, were twisted and tortured, and not without an anger that seemed to vibrate throughout the length and breadth of his massive frame. 'The moment you walked into Sam and Hilary's living-room, I said to myself—this is it! My time in Cape Town was limited, but I was determined to see as much of you as possible. I invited you to have dinner with me the following evening. Eventually I would have invited you to the farm. Your visit would have had to coincide with that of my parents to make it all respectable. But things worked out differently, didn't they?' His chest heaved as he drew his breath in sharply. 'You dropped an opportunity in my lap which I grasped with both hands. You were too darned attractive to leave about for someone else to snap up in my absence.'

'What are you saying?' she whispered hoarsely.

'I'm telling you that I love you,' he continued harshly. 'That I loved you from the first moment I saw you and, by heavens, if it's the last thing I do, I'll make you love me yet.'

The happiness that swept through her was intoxicatingly sweet. She lowered her lashes demurely with a confidence she had not known she possessed. 'And how, may I ask, do you propose to do that?'

'Like this!'

With obvious disregard for the pain and discomfort of his injury, his arms shot out and crushed her against him in a painful grip. Again and again he kissed her. Her lips, her eyes, her cheeks, the hollow in her throat where a tell-tale pulse leapt in response, and once again her lips. Vicky, responding deliriously to his fierce lovemaking, reached up and wound her arms about his neck, pushing her fingers through his crisp dark hair and stroking the back of his neck. His heart thudded violently against her and a tremor shook his tall frame.

He released her so suddenly that she staggered and was forced to grip the back of the chair for support.

'For God's sake, Vicky, you know I'll never keep you here against your will,' he exclaimed, his eyes leaping flames of passion, his great chest heaving, 'but don't play with fire unless you mean it. I've reached the end of my——'

He stopped suddenly and stared. The mask of polite indifference had been whipped from Vicky's face. Her eyes, large and luminous, no longer hid what lay in her heart, and Conrad stared into them like a drunken man who wished to drown himself in the message they conveyed.

'Vicky?' He took an uncertain step towards her, wincing once again as he bent his head to take a closer look.

Vicky drew a shuddering breath. 'Darling, I——'

She never finished her sentence, for she was instantly caught up against his chest in a grip that drove the breath from her body.

'Say that again!' he demanded, his voice hoarse with suppressed emotion.

'Darling.'

'Tell me it's true. Tell me you love me!'

181

'I love you,' she managed faintly. 'Oh, darling, I love you so terribly much.'

His kisses and caresses were suddenly so fierce that she was reduced to a trembling bundle of ecstasy in his arms. He pushed his fingers through her hair and sent the pins scattering to the floor before burying his face in its corn-coloured fragrance. Then, with a groan, he sought her lips once more.

'Vicky,' he whispered hoarsely against her throat. 'Sweet, darling, lovely Vicky.'

All this was sweet music to her ears as, stunned by the extent of her emotions, she could only cling to him rapturously as his lips caressed the softness of her shoulder with devastating effects.

'Conrad, please,' she protested weakly, warding off his conquering lips. 'We must talk sensibly for a moment, and you really should be lying down.'

Conrad laughed exultantly and released her. For a moment she felt too weak to stand on her own and she clutched at his shirt front for support, only to be scooped up in his arms once more. With tremendous diplomacy she managed to get him to lie down eventually.

'I shan't talk to you unless you do,' she had to threaten him, and he laughed, pulling her down to sit beside him on the bed.

'Talk away, sweetheart. I'm listening,' he said, running his hand caressingly up her bare arm and across her shoulder to the nape of her neck.

'How—how can I talk sensibly when you—you touch me like this?' she protested.

For a breathtaking second he stared at her with a mixture of laughter and love in his eyes before pulling her down against his broad chest and kissing her passionately and satisfyingly on the lips. He released her then and placed his hands behind his head.

'Is this better?'

She smiled tremulously. 'Much better.'

'Talk away, then.'

'I thought you were in love with Natalie.'

Conrad threw back his head and laughed uproariously. 'Natalie is a child who found it great fun at first experimenting in love,' he explained when he had managed to control himself. 'I was a staid old bachelor and handy to be used as a guinea-pig. She felt quite safe in the knowledge that I would never take her seriously.' He caught hold of her hand and raised it to his lips, caressing the delicate network of veins at her wrist. 'When did you know that you loved me?'

Vicky laughed then. 'That's the sort of question a woman usually asks.'

'That may be so,' he replied, quite unabashed, 'but you know already that I loved you from the start. What about you?'

'When I think back, I realise that I must have loved you from the beginning as well. You certainly had an alarming effect on my emotions, but . . .' She lowered her glance, her hair veiling her face. 'I knew for certain that I loved you on the eve of your parents' departure when I saw you in the garden with Natalie.'

The memory of that night sent a flash of pain across her sensitive face and, seeing it, Conrad instantly pulled her down into his arms and pressed her head on to his shoulder.

'Don't, my darling! Don't look like that,' he said contritely, dropping a kiss on to her hair and stroking her cheek. 'I owe you an explanation and, heaven knows, it's not going to be easy.'

For a time he was silent, brushing her cheek with his lips as though to stroke away the hurt he had inflicted, and when he started speaking his voice was low and tinged with remorse.

'Natalie wanted to speak to me privately that night. She said that it was urgent, and the only private place I could think of was the garden. She told me then that she was in love with Michael. Yes, don't look so surprised,' he added as Vicky glanced up at him swiftly. 'It's true.'

He pushed her head back on to his shoulder, running his fingers through her hair. Vicky closed her eyes as she rested against him, the steady beat of his heart beneath her ear, as she waited for him to continue.

'Natalie was in love with Michael and she was certain that he cared for her as well, but something held him back, so she suspected.'

'Does he care for her?' she interrupted to ask.

'Yes. Hadn't you noticed?'

'No. I suppose I was too occupied with my own problems.'

'To get back to what I was saying,' he continued. 'She asked me if I knew what it was that filled Michael with such restraint, and I told her.'

'Everything?'

'Yes.'

'About us as well?' She held her breath.

'No. That's between you and me.' He looked into her troubled eyes. 'She asked me whether she should confront him with this knowledge she had gleaned from me, or whether she should wait for him to tell her when he felt the time was right. I suggested she should wait, unless the situation became critical, then all three of us could have a serious discussion about it.' His arms tightened about her convulsively. 'Natalie cried a little and I comforted her as best I could. Then, when we entered the house, I saw you flirting with Rodney.'

'I was not flirting with him,' she protested from the depths of his shoulder. 'Well, perhaps just a little,' she conceded eventually.

'It certainly looked like it,' Conrad insisted. 'My desperation turned to anger, an anger that simmered throughout the rest of the evening. When we were finally alone you reacted to my tentative advances as though you found me loathsome and my anger became a white-hot rage.' He groaned and buried his face in her hair. 'I behaved like an unspeakable cad that night, Vicky, and I don't think I shall ever forget the look on your face. It's haunted me day and night ever since then.'

'Hush!' she cried, placing a silencing finger against his lips. 'Don't think about it again. I can understand and forgive.'

'But I shall never be able to forgive myself.' His lips trailed across her cheek and along the column of her throat. 'Many times I tried to apologise, but you wouldn't give me the opportunity. I can't find words adequate to express the loathing I felt for myself. Afterwards I tried in several ways to show you how sorry I was, but you seemed to slip further and further away from me. Then, last night, you came into the study and discovered that I'd been hurt.'

Vicky shuddered at the remembered sight.

'You were so concerned about me,' he went on, 'but I dared not even begin to hope that you could possibly care for me. I decided then that you would have been concerned about anyone in the same position as myself, and not simply because you cared for me. You confirmed that yourself, remember?' he added in a teasing tone of voice.

'Only because you more or less told me to my face that my concern was misplaced,' she reminded him. 'Oh, Conrad, I nearly died when I saw that awful wound!' she cried in anguish and Conrad instantly stilled her trembling lips beneath his own.

'Conrad,' she murmured much later, 'that photograph . . .'

'The one of you standing on the beach?'

She nodded against his shoulder. 'You said—you said——'

185

'That it revealed your true character,' he filled in for her, glancing at her strangely. 'Sam slipped that negative into my pocket on our wedding day. This was the wedding present Hilary mentioned in her letter. The confetti in my suitcase was there as well, so I actually spoke the truth, Sam said that day, and I recall his words vividly, "Vicky wanted me to destroy it, but I couldn't and kept it instead, knowing that the man who loved her would appreciate the beauty and simplicity of it".'

'It's the most embarrassing photograph,' she protested, her cheeks flaming.

'Shall I tell you what that photograph represented for me?' he said deliberately and, not waiting for her to reply, he continued, 'It represented innocence and beauty, and a warm, loving personality. There is also a hint of slumbering passion that would take the right man to awaken it. I prayed that I would be that man.'

Vicky could not believe her ears. 'Is—is that really what you saw?'

'Was there something else I should have seen?'

'Well—it—I don't know,' she ended lamely, her confusion making her blush even more.

'You thought that something in that photograph had given me the impression that you might have loose morals,' he guessed accurately, and when she admitted this his arms tightened about her and he kissed her with a passion that left her trembling. 'It was merely an unfortunate choice of words, spoken in a moment of anger when the intention was to lash out and hurt as much as I was being hurt.' He kissed her gently and lingeringly. 'Oh, what foolish people we've been! I have so much to atone for, my dearest heart, and I shall not blame you if you have no wish to continue with our marriage.'

'I don't wish to continue with it,' she told him firmly, a smile hovering about her lips as he held her away from him to glance at her anxiously. 'Not under the conditions you originally stipulated,' she added, her cheeks pink as she saw comprehension dawning in his eyes.

'What kind of marriage do you have in mind, then?' he asked teasingly, looking into her eyes and running a gentle finger along her warm cheek.

'I want a real marriage, Conrad,' she whispered tremulously, her pulse clamouring at the undisguised passion in his eyes. 'A real marriage to the devil who captured my heart at Devil's Gateway.'

'I can think of nothing more delightful,' he murmured, threading his fingers through her hair and drawing her head down to his to take the lips she offered so willingly.

The future was no longer uncertain and empty, but filled with the rapturous delight of loving Conrad, and knowing that she would for ever be secure in his love.

Did you miss any of these exciting Harlequin Omnibus 3-in-1 volumes?

Each volume contains 3 great novels by one author for only $1.95.
See order coupon.

Violet Winspear

Violet Winspear #3
The Cazalet Bride (#1434)
Beloved Castaway (#1472)
The Castle of the Seven Lilacs (#1514)

Anne Mather

Anne Mather
Charlotte's Hurricane (#1487)
Lord of Zaracus (#1574)
The Reluctant Governess (#1600)

Anne Hampson

Anne Hampson #1
Unwary Heart (#1388)
Precious Waif (#1420)
The Autocrat of Melhurst (#1442)

Betty Neels

Betty Neels
Tempestuous April (#1441)
Damsel in Green (#1465)
Tulips for Augusta (#1529)

Essie Summers

Essie Summers #3
Summer in December (#1416)
The Bay of the Nightingales (#1445)
Return to Dragonshill (#1502)

Margaret Way

Margaret Way
King Country (#1470)
Blaze of Silk (#1500)
The Man from Bahl Bahla (#1530)

---

40 magnificent Omnibus volumes to choose from:

Essie Summers #1
Bride in Flight (#933)
Postscript to Yesterday (#1119)
Meet on My Ground (#1326)

Jean S. MacLeod
The Wolf of Heimra (#990)
Summer Island (#1314)
Slave of the Wind (#1339)

Eleanor Farnes
The Red Cliffs (#1335)
The Flight of the Swan (#1280)
Sister of the Housemaster (#975)

Susan Barrie #1
Marry a Stranger (#1034)
Rose in the Bud (#1168)
The Marriage Wheel (#1311)

Violet Winspear #1
Beloved Tyrant (#1032)
Court of the Veils (#1267)
Palace of the Peacocks (#1318)

Isobel Chace
The Saffron Sky (#1250)
A Handful of Silver (#1306)
The Damask Rose (#1334)

Joyce Dingwell #1
Will You Surrender (#1179)
A Taste for Love (#1229)
The Feel of Silk (#1342)

Sara Seale
Queen of Hearts (#1324)
Penny Plain (#1197)
Green Girl (#1045)

Jane Arbor
A Girl Named Smith (#1000)
Kingfisher Tide (#950)
The Cypress Garden (#1336)

Anne Weale
The Sea Waif (#1123)
The Feast of Sara (#1007)
Doctor in Malaya (#914)

Essie Summers #2
His Serene Miss Smith (#1093)
The Master to Tawhai (#910)
A Place Called Paradise (#1156)

Catherine Airlie
Doctor Overboard (#979)
Nobody's Child (#1258)
A Wind Sighing (#1328)

Violet Winspear #2
Bride's Dilemma (#1008)
Tender Is the Tyrant (#1208)
The Dangerous Delight (#1344)

Kathryn Blair
Doctor Westland (#954)
Battle of Love (#1038)
Flowering Wilderness (#1148)

Rosalind Brett
The Girl at White Drift (#1101)
Winds of Enchantment (#1176)
Brittle Bondage (#1319)

Rose Burghley
Man of Destiny (#960)
The Sweet Surrender (#1023)
The Bay of Moonlight (#1245)

Iris Danbury
Rendezvous in Lisbon (#1178)
Doctor at Villa Ronda (#1257)
Hotel Belvedere (#1331)

Amanda Doyle
A Change for Clancy (#1085)
Play the Tune Softly (#1116)
A Mist in Glen Torran (#1308)

Great value in Reading!
Use the handy order form

Elizabeth Hoy
Snare the Wild Heart (#992)
The Faithless One (#1104)
Be More than Dreams (#1286)

Roumelia Lane
House of the Winds (#1262)
A Summer to Love (#1280)
Sea of Zanj (#1338)

Margaret Malcolm
The Master of Normanhurst (#1028)
The Man in Homespun (#1140)
Meadowsweet (#1164)

Joyce Dingwell #2
The Timber Man (#917)
Project Sweetheart (#964)
Greenfingers Farm (#999)

Marjorie Norell
Nurse Madeline of Eden Grove (#962)
Thank You, Nurse Conway (#1097)
The Marriage of Doctor Royle (#1177)

Anne Durham
New Doctor at Northmoor (#1242)
Nurse Sally's Last Chance (#1281)
Mann of the Medical Wing (#1313)

Henrietta Reid
Reluctant Masquerade (#1380)
Hunter's Moon (#1430)
The Black Delaney (#1460)

Lucy Gillen
The Silver Fishes (#1408)
Heir to Glen Ghyll (#1450)
The Girl at Smuggler's Rest (#1533)

Anne Hampson #2
When the Bough Breaks (#1491)
Love Hath an Island (#1522)
Stars of Spring (#1551)

Essie Summers #4
No Legacy for Lindsay (#957)
No Orchids by Request (#982)
Sweet Are the Ways (#1015)

Mary Burchell #3
The Other Linding Girl (#1431)
Girl with a Challenge (#1455)
My Sister Celia (#1474)

Susan Barrie #2
Return to Tremarth (#1359)
Night of the Singing Birds (#1428)
Bride in Waiting (#1526)

Violet Winspear #4
Desert Doctor (#921)
The Viking Stranger (#1080)
The Tower of the Captive (#1111)

Essie Summers #5
Heir to Windrush Hill (#1055)
Rosalind Comes Home (#1283)
Revolt — and Virginia (#1348)

Doris E. Smith
To Sing Me Home (#1427)
Seven of Magpies (#1454)
Dear Deceiver (#1599)

Katrina Britt
Healer of Hearts (#1393)
The Fabulous Island (#1490)
A Spray of Edelweiss (#1626)

Betty Neels #2
Sister Peters in Amsterdam (#1361)
Nurse in Holland (#1385)
Blow Hot — Blow Cold (#1409)

Amanda Doyle #2
The Girl for Gillgong (#1351)
The Year at Yattabilla (#1448)
Kookaburra Dawn (#1562)

Complete and mail this coupon today!

Send coupon today for
FREE
Harlequin Presents Catalog

We'll send you by return mail a complete listing of all the wonderful Harlequin Presents novels still in stock.

Here's your chance to catch up on all the delightful reading you may have missed because the books are no longer available at your favorite booksellers.

Fill in this handy order form and mail it today.